Intro

The fact you're reading this says a lot about you and the priority you place on your health and wellbeing. This makes my heart sing.

Before you get into the journal, I thought I'd share a few words about its background, why I created it, and my hope for you as you use it.

The journal is born out of my passion to see women live well in holistic health and wellbeing, especially midlife women, whom I serve. I see too many of us busy rushing around taking care of family, profession, business, ministry and everyone else in between when, at this stage when we should start winding down and enjoying life, many are bogged down with chronic illness or unmanageable menopausal symptoms. It really doesn't have to be this way.

I firmly believe that without optimal physical and mental capacity we can't really achieve much, and so taking care of our health and wellbeing should be our number one priority. We can't pour from an empty cup. We have many "to-do" lists and are intentional about most things except ourselves. I created the journal as a tool to help change this.

My intention for you and the journal is to:
- Help you prioritise "Self".
- Have it form part of your daily self-care routine.
- Help you become intentional about your health and wellbeing; you do not just write in the journal but complete the "Action Items" too.
- Practice journaling and reap its benefits.
- Practice gratitude and reap its benefits.
- Practice meditation and reap its benefits.
- Partner with God to take responsibility for your health and wellbeing.

The journal is undated and features a wide range of health and wellbeing topics, covering a different topic each week. I felt the weekly timeframe would give more time to focus on a particular topic and help you to embed or change certain behaviours. You can choose to start wherever you like.

With the journal, you'll promote your sense of wellbeing as you shift to a more positive state of mind. You'll hone your ability to focus on the good things happening in your life.

The easy-to-use format and action items will guide you toward a more holistic sense of wellbeing. I encourage you to begin and end each day with the journal; use it to set your intentions for the day, meditating on the word, then end the day with a short prayer, moments of reflection and a chance to capture your gratitude. This daily practice will help you create a pattern of self-care within your busy lives.

The good book says, "Beloved I pray that you may prosper in all things and be in health; just as your soul prospers" 3John1:2. It is my fervent prayer that, as you actively engage with and use the journal, it shall be so for you! Amen

To your Wellbeing! Love and Blessings, Bukky x

Dedication

YOUR MIDLIFE ~ HAPPY, HEALTHY, WELL

This Journal is Dedicated to:

God My Father - The source and inspiration of all I do

My wonderful children - Afolake & Oladayo

My family, friends, clients & associates too numerous to mention

Midlife Women Worldwide - May you live happy, healthy & well!

Weekly Topics

Weeks 1 & 26 - Faith
Weeks 2 & 28 - Love
Weeks 3 & 29 - Diet
Weeks 4, 30 & 42 - Exercise
Weeks 5 & 31 - Stress
Weeks 6 & 32 - Sleep
Weeks 7 & 33 - Relationships
Week 8 - Substance Use
Weeks 9 & 34 - Weight
Weeks 10 & 35 - Your Mind
Week 36 - Anxiety
Weeks 11 & 37 - Self Care
Weeks 12 & 38 - Self Esteem
Weeks 13 & 47 - Purpose
Weeks 14 & 39 - Wealth
Weeks 15 & 40 - Success
Weeks 16 & 46 - Peace
Weeks 17 & 45 - Health & Healing
Weeks 18 & 43 - Hope
Weeks 19 & 44 - Joy
Weeks 20 & 48 - Confidence
Weeks 21 & 49 - Vision
Weeks 22 & 50 - Emotions
Weeks 23 & 41 - Energy
Weeks 24 & 51 - Contentment
Week 52 - Thanksgiving

• WEEK 1 • FAITH •

AFFIRMATIONS

I RELY ON GOD TO HELP ME MAKE THE CHANGES I DESIRE IN MY HEALTH AND WELLBEING

AS I RELY ON GOD AND TRUST HIM, HE GIVES ME THE ABILITY AND POWER TO MAKE THE LIFESTYLE CHANGES I WANT

I RELAX IN GOD'S GRACE TO HELP ME ACHIEVE THE CHANGES I WANT TO SEE IN MY HEALTH AND WELLBEING

I WILL NOT RELY ON MY WILLPOWER BUT CHOOSE TO HAVE FAITH IN GOD TO HELP ME LIVE A LIFE OF HEALTH, BALANCE AND WELLBEING

MEDITATION

GOD SAYS "I CAN DO ALL THIS THROUGH HIM WHO GIVES ME STRENGTH"
PHIL 4:13 NIV

"Faith is taking the first step, even when you don't see the whole staircase"
Martin Luther King Jnr

Weekly Thought/Action

WRITE DOWN ANY HEALTH OR WELLBEING GOALS YOU ARE
TRUSTING GOD FOR AT THIS TIME.

DATE _____

_____
_____
_____
_____

DATE _____

_____
_____
_____
_____

DATE _____

_____
_____
_____
_____

DATE _____

_____
_____
_____
_____

DATE _____

_____
_____
_____
_____

DATE _____

_____
_____
_____
_____

DATE _____

_____
_____
_____
_____

WEEKLY GRATITUDE

DATE _____

I'M GRATEFUL FOR....

1. _____
2. _____
3. _____

DATE _____

I'M GRATEFUL FOR....

1. _____
2. _____
3. _____

DATE _____

I'M GRATEFUL FOR....

1. _____
2. _____
3. _____

DATE _____

I'M GRATEFUL FOR....

1. _____
2. _____
3. _____

DATE _____

I'M GRATEFUL FOR....

1. _____
2. _____
3. _____

DATE _____

I'M GRATEFUL FOR....

1. _____
2. _____
3. _____

DATE _____

I'M GRATEFUL FOR....

1. _____
2. _____
3. _____

• WEEK 2 • LOVE •

AFFIRMATIONS

I AM FILLED WITH LOVE IN MY HEART FOR MYSELF AND OTHERS

I AM GUIDED BY LOVE

I AM BURSTING WITH LOVE

I RECEIVE LOVE EASILY AND WITH GRATITUDE

MEDITATION

"...LOVE YOUR NEIGHBOUR AS YOURSELF"
MATT 22:39NIV

"Love makes the world go round; family makes the ride worthwhile"
Unknown

Weekly Thought/Action

EACH DAY, WRITE DOWN 3 THINGS YOU LOVE ABOUT YOURSELF

DATE _____

_____

_____

_____

_____

DATE _____

_____

_____

_____

_____

DATE _____

_____

_____

_____

_____

DATE _____

_____

_____

_____

_____

DATE _____

_____

_____

_____

_____

DATE _____

_____

_____

_____

_____

DATE _____

_____

_____

_____

_____

WEEKLY GRATITUDE

DATE _____

I'M GRATEFUL FOR....

1. _____
2. _____
3. _____

DATE _____

I'M GRATEFUL FOR....

1. _____
2. _____
3. _____

DATE _____

I'M GRATEFUL FOR....

1. _____
2. _____
3. _____

DATE _____

I'M GRATEFUL FOR....

1. _____
2. _____
3. _____

DATE _____

I'M GRATEFUL FOR....

1. _____
2. _____
3. _____

DATE _____

I'M GRATEFUL FOR....

1. _____
2. _____
3. _____

DATE _____

I'M GRATEFUL FOR....

1. _____
2. _____
3. _____

• WEEK 3 • DIET •

AFFIRMATIONS

MY HEALTH IS IMPORTANT TO ME AND I AM
MAKING HEALTHY ALTERATIONS TO MY DIET

I AM MAKING POSITIVE CHANGES TO MY
NUTRITION WHICH ENERGIZES ME

I FEEL ENERGISED AND ALIVE BY THE POSITIVE
CHANGES TO MY FOOD INTAKE

I FOCUS ON WELLNESS AND RECOGNISE I MUST
EAT HEALTHY FOODS TO BE WELL

MEDITATION

GOD SAYS "I GIVE YOU EVERY SEED-BEARING PLANT ON
THE FACE OF THE WHOLE EARTH AND EVERY TREE
THAT HAS FRUIT WITH SEED IN IT. THEY WILL BE YOURS
FOR FOOD"
GEN 1:29 NIV

"Let thy food be medicine
and medicine be thy food"
Hippocrates

WEEKLY THOUGHT/ACTION

LIST THE FOODS YOU EAT NOW. ARE YOU HAPPY WITH THIS LIST OR DO YOU WANT TO MAKE SOME CHANGES? IF SO, WHAT CHANGES WOULD YOU LIKE TO MAKE?

DATE _____

_____
_____
_____
_____

DATE _____

_____
_____
_____
_____

DATE _____

_____
_____
_____
_____

DATE _____

_____
_____
_____
_____

DATE _____

_____
_____
_____
_____

DATE _____

_____
_____
_____
_____

DATE _____

_____
_____
_____
_____

WEEKLY GRATITUDE

DATE _____

I'M GRATEFUL FOR....

1. _____
2. _____
3. _____

DATE _____

I'M GRATEFUL FOR....

1. _____
2. _____
3. _____

DATE _____

I'M GRATEFUL FOR....

1. _____
2. _____
3. _____

DATE _____

I'M GRATEFUL FOR....

1. _____
2. _____
3. _____

DATE _____

I'M GRATEFUL FOR....

1. _____
2. _____
3. _____

DATE _____

I'M GRATEFUL FOR....

1. _____
2. _____
3. _____

DATE _____

I'M GRATEFUL FOR....

1. _____
2. _____
3. _____

• WEEK 4 • EXERCISE •

AFFIRMATIONS

I STAY PHYSICALLY ACTIVE TO STRENGTHEN MY
BODY AND MIND

MY EXERCISE STRENGTHENS MY BONES AND
BUILDS UP MY ENDURANCE

I EXERCISE CONSISTENTLY AND MAKE IT PART
OF MY DAILY ROUTINE

I FEEL FIT AND ENERGETIC

Meditation

GOD SAYS "I DISCIPLINE MY BODY LIKE AN ATHLETE,
TRAINING IT TO DO WHAT IT SHOULD. OTHERWISE, I
FEAR THAT AFTER PREACHING TO OTHERS I MYSELF
MIGHT BE DISQUALIFIED"
I COR 9: 27 NLT

"Exercise should be regarded
as a tribute to the heart"
Gene Tunney

WEEKLY THOUGHT/ACTION

WRITE DOWN WHAT YOU CURRENTLY DO FOR EXERCISE. WHICH EXERCISE/S DO YOU ENJOY? WHICH WOULD YOU LIKE TO DO MORE? HOW COULD YOU MAKE THIS HAPPEN?

DATE _____

_____
_____
_____
_____

DATE _____

_____
_____
_____
_____

DATE _____

_____
_____
_____
_____

DATE _____

_____
_____
_____
_____

DATE _____

_____
_____
_____
_____

DATE _____

_____
_____
_____
_____

DATE _____

_____
_____
_____
_____

WEEKLY GRATITUDE

DATE _____

I'M GRATEFUL FOR....

1. _____
2. _____
3. _____

DATE _____

I'M GRATEFUL FOR....

1. _____
2. _____
3. _____

DATE _____

I'M GRATEFUL FOR....

1. _____
2. _____
3. _____

DATE _____

I'M GRATEFUL FOR....

1. _____
2. _____
3. _____

DATE _____

I'M GRATEFUL FOR....

1. _____
2. _____
3. _____

DATE _____

I'M GRATEFUL FOR....

1. _____
2. _____
3. _____

DATE _____

I'M GRATEFUL FOR....

1. _____
2. _____
3. _____

• WEEK 5 • STRESS •

AFFIRMATIONS

I RELY ON PRAYER AND MEDITATION AS MY ROCK DURING STRESSFUL MOMENTS

I PRAY AND MEDITATE TO CONNECT TO THE SOURCE OF PEACE IN STRESSFUL TIMES

I BREATHE IN PEACE AND BREATHE OUT STRESS FROM MY LIFE

I AM THANKFUL I CAN PRAY AS A WAY TO CLEAR MY MIND AND ORGANISE MY THOUGHTS AT STRESSFUL TIMES

MEDITATION

GOD SAYS – "CAST ALL YOUR ANXIETY ON HIM BECAUSE HE CARES FOR YOU.
1PET 5:7 NIV

"The greatest weapon against stress is our ability to choose one thought over another".
William James

WEEKLY THOUGHT/ACTION
HOW CAN YOU INCREASE THE TIME YOU SPEND IN PRAYER & MEDITATION TO AVOID STRESS IN YOUR LIFE?
WHAT ACTIONS CAN YOU TAKE NOW?

DATE _____

_____
_____
_____
_____

DATE _____

_____
_____
_____
_____

DATE _____

_____
_____
_____
_____

DATE _____

_____
_____
_____
_____

DATE _____

_____
_____
_____
_____

DATE _____

_____
_____
_____
_____

DATE _____

_____
_____
_____
_____

WEEKLY GRATITUDE

DATE _____

I'M GRATEFUL FOR....

1. _____
2. _____
3. _____

DATE _____

I'M GRATEFUL FOR....

1. _____
2. _____
3. _____

DATE _____

I'M GRATEFUL FOR....

1. _____
2. _____
3. _____

DATE _____

I'M GRATEFUL FOR....

1. _____
2. _____
3. _____

DATE _____

I'M GRATEFUL FOR....

1. _____
2. _____
3. _____

DATE _____

I'M GRATEFUL FOR....

1. _____
2. _____
3. _____

DATE _____

I'M GRATEFUL FOR....

1. _____
2. _____
3. _____

• WEEK 6 • SLEEP •

AFFIRMATIONS

I AM PROACTIVE WHEN IT COMES TO MY SLEEP,
SO THAT I SLEEP WELL

I ESTABLISH RELAXATION HABITS THAT SET ME
UP FOR A PEACEFUL NIGHT'S SLEEP

I SLEEP PEACEFULLY SO I WAKE UP FULLY ALERT
AND REFRESHED

MY EVENING ROUTINE IS RELAXED
AND PREPARES MY MIND AND BODY
FOR GOOD SLEEP

MEDITATION

GOD SAYS " I LIE DOWN AND SLEEP; I WAKE AGAIN,
BECAUSE THE LORD SUSTAINS ME".
PS 3:5 NIV

"Tired minds don't plan well; sleep first, plan later"
Walter Reisch

Weekly Thought/Action

WHAT CAN YOU DO TO IMPROVE THE QUALITY OF YOUR SLEEP?
WHAT CAN YOU START OR STOP DOING NOW
TO GET BETTER SLEEP?

DATE _____

_____
_____
_____
_____

DATE _____

_____
_____
_____
_____

DATE _____

_____
_____
_____
_____

DATE _____

_____
_____
_____
_____

DATE _____

_____
_____
_____
_____

DATE _____

_____
_____
_____
_____

DATE _____

_____
_____
_____
_____

WEEKLY GRATITUDE

DATE _____

I'M GRATEFUL FOR....

1. _____
2. _____
3. _____

DATE _____

I'M GRATEFUL FOR....

1. _____
2. _____
3. _____

DATE _____

I'M GRATEFUL FOR....

1. _____
2. _____
3. _____

DATE _____

I'M GRATEFUL FOR....

1. _____
2. _____
3. _____

DATE _____

I'M GRATEFUL FOR....

1. _____
2. _____
3. _____

DATE _____

I'M GRATEFUL FOR....

1. _____
2. _____
3. _____

DATE _____

I'M GRATEFUL FOR....

1. _____
2. _____
3. _____

• WEEK 7 • RELATIONSHIPS •

AFFIRMATIONS

I AM GRATEFUL I HAVE RELATIONSHIPS WHICH ARE HEALTHY AND THRIVING

I AM GRATEFUL FOR THE LOVE OF MY HUSBAND/ PARTNER/ OR SIGNIFICANT OTHER

I HAVE LOVING, STABLE AND SUPPORTIVE RELATIONSHIPS WITH MY FAMILY AND FRIENDS

I CHERISH MY FRIENDS, FAMILY, AND WORK ASSOCIATES, EACH IN THEIR OWN WAY

MEDITATION

GOD SAYS: "A NEW COMMAND I GIVE YOU: LOVE ONE ANOTHER. AS I HAVE LOVED YOU, SO YOU MUST LOVE ONE ANOTHER"
JOHN 13:34 NIV

"The best time to make friends is before you need them"
Ethel Barrymore

Weekly Thought/Action

WHICH OF YOUR CONNECTIONS COULD USE A LITTLE ATTENTION?
WHO WILL YOU SEND A MESSAGE TO OR CALL THIS WEEK?
REACH OUT TO SOMEONE EACH DAY THIS WEEK

DATE _____

_____
_____
_____
_____

DATE _____

_____
_____
_____
_____

DATE _____

_____
_____
_____
_____

DATE _____

_____
_____
_____
_____

DATE _____

_____
_____
_____
_____

DATE _____

_____
_____
_____
_____

DATE _____

_____
_____
_____
_____

WEEKLY GRATITUDE

DATE _____

I'M GRATEFUL FOR....

1. _____
2. _____
3. _____

DATE _____

I'M GRATEFUL FOR....

1. _____
2. _____
3. _____

DATE _____

I'M GRATEFUL FOR....

1. _____
2. _____
3. _____

DATE _____

I'M GRATEFUL FOR....

1. _____
2. _____
3. _____

DATE _____

I'M GRATEFUL FOR....

1. _____
2. _____
3. _____

DATE _____

I'M GRATEFUL FOR....

1. _____
2. _____
3. _____

DATE _____

I'M GRATEFUL FOR....

1. _____
2. _____
3. _____

• WEEK 8 • SUBSTANCE USE •

AFFIRMATIONS

I CHOOSE TO BREAK AWAY FROM A
DEPENDENCY ON HARMFUL SUBSTANCES LIKE
DRUGS, ALCOHOL OR TOBACCO

I WILL NOT USE HARMFUL SUBSTANCES TO
COPE WITH STRESSFUL SITUATIONS

I AM TEETOTAL OR DRINK ALCOHOL IN
MODERATION

AS I RESIST OR LIMIT THE USE OF ALCOHOL AND
TOBACCO, I WARD OFF CHRONIC DISEASE

MEDITATION

"DO YOU NOT KNOW THAT YOUR BODIES ARE
TEMPLES OF THE HOLY SPIRIT, WHO IS IN YOU,
WHOM YOU HAVE RECEIVED FROM GOD? YOU
ARE NOT YOUR OWN"
I COR 6:19 NIV

"I have to take care of myself.
It's about self-preservation"
Danielle de Niese

Weekly Thought/Action

WHAT CAN YOU DO NOW TO KICK ANY HABITS YOU HAVE WITH
CIGARETTES, ALCOHOL OR DRUGS?
WHO/WHERE CAN YOU ASK FOR HELP?

DATE _____

_____
_____
_____
_____

DATE _____

_____
_____
_____
_____

DATE _____

_____
_____
_____
_____

DATE _____

_____
_____
_____
_____

DATE _____

_____
_____
_____
_____

DATE _____

_____
_____
_____
_____

DATE _____

_____
_____
_____
_____

WEEKLY GRATITUDE

DATE _____

I'M GRATEFUL FOR....

1. _____
2. _____
3. _____

DATE _____

I'M GRATEFUL FOR....

1. _____
2. _____
3. _____

DATE _____

I'M GRATEFUL FOR....

1. _____
2. _____
3. _____

DATE _____

I'M GRATEFUL FOR....

1. _____
2. _____
3. _____

DATE _____

I'M GRATEFUL FOR....

1. _____
2. _____
3. _____

DATE _____

I'M GRATEFUL FOR....

1. _____
2. _____
3. _____

DATE _____

I'M GRATEFUL FOR....

1. _____
2. _____
3. _____

• WEEK 9 • WEIGHT •

AFFIRMATIONS

AS I EAT HEALTHILY AND EXERCISE; MY BODY ACHIEVES A WEIGHT THAT IS HEALTHY FOR ME

I TAKE MY BODY WEIGHT AND HEALTH SERIOUSLY

I MAINTAIN A HEALTHY BODY WEIGHT

TODAY, I ENJOY MY HEALTHY BODY WEIGHT

MEDITATION

GOD SAYS: "THEREFORE, I URGE YOU, BROTHERS AND SISTERS, IN VIEW OF GOD'S MERCY, TO OFFER YOUR BODIES AS A LIVING SACRIFICE, HOLY AND PLEASING TO GOD—THIS IS YOUR TRUE AND PROPER WORSHIP".
ROM 12:1 NIV

"The secret of losing weight is Patience".
Jane Fonda

WEEKLY THOUGHT/ACTION

FIND OUT - WHAT IS YOUR HEALTHY BODY WEIGHT?
WHAT IS YOUR WAIST:HIP RATIO (<0.85 GOAL)? WHAT OTHER
THOUGHTS/GOALS DO YOU HAVE ABOUT YOUR WEIGHT?

DATE _____

_____

_____

_____

_____

DATE _____

_____

_____

_____

_____

DATE _____

_____

_____

_____

_____

DATE _____

_____

_____

_____

_____

DATE _____

_____

_____

_____

_____

DATE _____

_____

_____

_____

_____

DATE _____

_____

_____

_____

_____

WEEKLY GRATITUDE

DATE _____

I'M GRATEFUL FOR....

1. _____
2. _____
3. _____

DATE _____

I'M GRATEFUL FOR....

1. _____
2. _____
3. _____

DATE _____

I'M GRATEFUL FOR....

1. _____
2. _____
3. _____

DATE _____

I'M GRATEFUL FOR....

1. _____
2. _____
3. _____

DATE _____

I'M GRATEFUL FOR....

1. _____
2. _____
3. _____

DATE _____

I'M GRATEFUL FOR....

1. _____
2. _____
3. _____

DATE _____

I'M GRATEFUL FOR....

1. _____
2. _____
3. _____

• WEEK 10 • YOUR MIND •

AFFIRMATIONS

MY MIND IS SATURATED WITH POSITIVE
THOUGHTS AND IDEAS

MY INNERMOST THOUGHTS REVOLVE AROUND
GOOD

I ONLY THINK THOUGHTS OF HOPE AND
ENCOURAGEMENT

I DO NOT ALLOW CRITICISM OR NEGATIVE
THOUGHTS TO PENETRATE THE WALLS OF MY
MIND

MEDITATION

GOD SAYS:" …AND NOW, DEAR BROTHERS AND SISTERS,
ONE FINAL THING. FIX YOUR THOUGHTS ON WHAT IS
TRUE, AND HONOURABLE, AND RIGHT, AND PURE, AND
LOVELY, AND ADMIRABLE. THINK ABOUT THINGS THAT
ARE EXCELLENT AND WORTHY OF PRAISE"
PHIL 4:8 NLT

"Your strongest muscle and your
worst enemy is your mind; train it well"
Unknown

Weekly Thought/Action

WHAT CAN/WILL YOU DO THIS WEEK TO STRENGTHEN YOUR MIND?
LIST SOMETHING DIFFERENT FOR EACH DAY

DATE _____

_____

_____

_____

_____

DATE _____

_____

_____

_____

_____

DATE _____

_____

_____

_____

_____

DATE _____

_____

_____

_____

_____

DATE _____

_____

_____

_____

_____

DATE _____

_____

_____

_____

_____

DATE _____

_____

_____

_____

_____

WEEKLY GRATITUDE

DATE _____

I'M GRATEFUL FOR....

1. _____
2. _____
3. _____

DATE _____

I'M GRATEFUL FOR....

1. _____
2. _____
3. _____

DATE _____

I'M GRATEFUL FOR....

1. _____
2. _____
3. _____

DATE _____

I'M GRATEFUL FOR....

1. _____
2. _____
3. _____

DATE _____

I'M GRATEFUL FOR....

1. _____
2. _____
3. _____

DATE _____

I'M GRATEFUL FOR....

1. _____
2. _____
3. _____

DATE _____

I'M GRATEFUL FOR....

1. _____
2. _____
3. _____

• WEEK 11 • SELF CARE •

AFFIRMATIONS

TODAY AND EVERY DAY, I MAKE MYSELF A TOP PRIORITY

MY SELF-CARE IS IMPORTANT, SO I TREAT MYSELF WELL

I SEEK OUT THINGS I ENJOY AND LOVE TO DO AND DO THEM TO TREAT MYSELF

I PRACTICE HABITS AND BEHAVIOURS THAT INVEST IN MYSELF

MEDITATION

GOD SAYS "......LOVE YOUR NEIGHBOUR AS YOU DO YOURSELF"
MATT 19:18 MSG

"Self-care is giving the world what's best of you, instead of what's left of you"
Katie Reed

Weekly Thought/Action

WHAT CAN YOU DO THIS WEEK TO SHOW YOURSELF YOU ARE IMPORTANT?

DATE _____

_____
_____
_____
_____

DATE _____

_____
_____
_____
_____

DATE _____

_____
_____
_____
_____

DATE _____

_____
_____
_____
_____

DATE _____

_____
_____
_____
_____

DATE _____

_____
_____
_____
_____

DATE _____

_____
_____
_____
_____

WEEKLY GRATITUDE

DATE _____

I'M GRATEFUL FOR....

1. _____
2. _____
3. _____

DATE _____

I'M GRATEFUL FOR....

1. _____
2. _____
3. _____

DATE _____

I'M GRATEFUL FOR....

1. _____
2. _____
3. _____

DATE _____

I'M GRATEFUL FOR....

1. _____
2. _____
3. _____

DATE _____

I'M GRATEFUL FOR....

1. _____
2. _____
3. _____

DATE _____

I'M GRATEFUL FOR....

1. _____
2. _____
3. _____

DATE _____

I'M GRATEFUL FOR....

1. _____
2. _____
3. _____

• WEEK 12 • SELF ESTEEM •

AFFIRMATIONS

I HAVE A HEALTHY LEVEL OF SELF-ESTEEM

MY SELF-ESTEEM INCREASES WITH EACH PASSING DAY

I DESERVE TO FEEL GOOD ABOUT MYSELF

MY HIGH LEVEL OF SELF-ESTEEM ATTRACTS PEOPLE TO ME

MEDITATION

GOD SAYS: "FOR YOU CREATED MY INMOST BEING; YOU KNIT ME TOGETHER IN MY MOTHER'S WOMB. I PRAISE YOU BECAUSE I AM FEARFULLY AND WONDERFULLY MADE; YOUR WORKS ARE WONDERFUL; I KNOW THAT FULL WELL".
PS 139:13-14 NIV

"Self-esteem is a powerful force within each of us... Self-esteem is the experience that we are appropriate to life and to the requirements of life"
Nathaniel Branden

Weekly Thought/Action

EACH DAY, WRITE DOWN 3 QUALITIES
YOU ADMIRE ABOUT YOURSELF?   USE "I AM" STATEMENTS

DATE _____

_____
_____
_____
_____

DATE _____

_____
_____
_____
_____

DATE _____

_____
_____
_____
_____

DATE _____

_____
_____
_____
_____

DATE _____

_____
_____
_____
_____

DATE _____

_____
_____
_____
_____

DATE _____

_____
_____
_____
_____

WEEKLY GRATITUDE

DATE _____

I'M GRATEFUL FOR....

1. _____
2. _____
3. _____

DATE _____

I'M GRATEFUL FOR....

1. _____
2. _____
3. _____

DATE _____

I'M GRATEFUL FOR....

1. _____
2. _____
3. _____

DATE _____

I'M GRATEFUL FOR....

1. _____
2. _____
3. _____

DATE _____

I'M GRATEFUL FOR....

1. _____
2. _____
3. _____

DATE _____

I'M GRATEFUL FOR....

1. _____
2. _____
3. _____

DATE _____

I'M GRATEFUL FOR....

1. _____
2. _____
3. _____

• WEEK 13 • PURPOSE •

AFFIRMATIONS

I AM HERE ON EARTH FOR A REASON AND I AM FULFILLING MY PURPOSE

I MAKE MY PLANS, BUT GOD'S PURPOSE WILL PREVAIL

EACH DAY GIVES ME THE OPPORTUNITY TO BE RADIANTLY ALIVE

I AM AWARE GOD IS WORKING IN ME, GIVING ME THE DESIRE AND POWER TO DO HIS WILL

MEDITATION

"AND WE KNOW THAT IN ALL THINGS GOD WORKS FOR THE GOOD OF THOSE WHO LOVE HIM, WHO HAVE BEEN CALLED ACCORDING TO HIS PURPOSE".
ROM 8:28 NKJV

"Find out who you are. And do it on purpose".
Dolly Parton

Weekly Thought/Action

CONSIDER AND WRITE DOWN WHAT IS MOST IMPORTANT TO YOU.
WHAT WOULD MAKE YOU FEEL MOST FULFILLED?
WHAT BIG DREAMS DO YOU HAVE?

DATE _____

_____
_____
_____
_____

DATE _____

_____
_____
_____
_____

DATE _____

_____
_____
_____
_____

DATE _____

_____
_____
_____
_____

DATE _____

_____
_____
_____
_____

DATE _____

_____
_____
_____
_____

DATE _____

_____
_____
_____
_____

WEEKLY GRATITUDE

DATE _____

I'M GRATEFUL FOR....

1. _____
2. _____
3. _____

DATE _____

I'M GRATEFUL FOR....

1. _____
2. _____
3. _____

DATE _____

I'M GRATEFUL FOR....

1. _____
2. _____
3. _____

DATE _____

I'M GRATEFUL FOR....

1. _____
2. _____
3. _____

DATE _____

I'M GRATEFUL FOR....

1. _____
2. _____
3. _____

DATE _____

I'M GRATEFUL FOR....

1. _____
2. _____
3. _____

DATE _____

I'M GRATEFUL FOR....

1. _____
2. _____
3. _____

• WEEK 14 • WEALTH •

AFFIRMATIONS

I AM FILLED WITH THE KNOWLEDGE OF GODS WILL, HIS WILL IS MY PROSPERITY

I AM HAPPY AND GRATEFUL THAT MONEY COMES TO ME IN INCREASING QUANTITIES, FROM A VARIETY OF SOURCES ON A CONSISTENT BASIS

I HAVE THE POWER TO GET WEALTH AND GOD CANCELS ALL MY DEBTS

I AM BLESSED; AS GOD IS THE UNFAILING UNLIMITED SOURCE OF MY SUPPLY

MEDITATION

"HONOUR THE LORD WITH YOUR WEALTH, WITH THE FIRST-FRUITS OF ALL YOUR CROPS, THEN YOUR BARNS WILL BE FILLED TO OVERFLOWING, AND YOUR VATS WILL BRIM OVER WITH NEW WINE"
PROV 3: 9-10 NIV

"Without a rich heart,
wealth is an ugly beggar"
Ralph Waldo Emerson

Weekly Thought/Action

WRITE DOWN ALL YOUR INCOME SOURCES
AND PRAY FOR GOD'S BLESSING ON EACH OF THEM.
LIST OTHER WAYS YOU CAN INCREASE YOUR INCOME.

DATE _____

_____
_____
_____
_____

DATE _____

_____
_____
_____
_____

DATE _____

_____
_____
_____
_____

DATE _____

_____
_____
_____
_____

DATE _____

_____
_____
_____
_____

DATE _____

_____
_____
_____
_____

DATE _____

_____
_____
_____
_____

WEEKLY GRATITUDE

DATE _____

I'M GRATEFUL FOR....

1. _____
2. _____
3. _____

DATE _____

I'M GRATEFUL FOR....

1. _____
2. _____
3. _____

DATE _____

I'M GRATEFUL FOR....

1. _____
2. _____
3. _____

DATE _____

I'M GRATEFUL FOR....

1. _____
2. _____
3. _____

DATE _____

I'M GRATEFUL FOR....

1. _____
2. _____
3. _____

DATE _____

I'M GRATEFUL FOR....

1. _____
2. _____
3. _____

DATE _____

I'M GRATEFUL FOR....

1. _____
2. _____
3. _____

• WEEK 15 • SUCCESS •

AFFIRMATIONS

I STUDY, MEDITATE AND OBEY GOD'S WORD AND SO I PROSPER AND HAVE GOOD SUCCESS

I AM FREE TO ENJOY MY LIFE AND SUCCESS

I FOCUS ON SUCCESS AND NOT FAILURES IN ALL MY ENDEAVOURS

GOD MAKES ME SUCCESSFUL IN EVERYTHING I DO

MEDITATION

...." KEEP THIS BOOK OF THE LAW ALWAYS ON YOUR LIPS; MEDITATE ON IT DAY AND NIGHT, SO THAT YOU MAY BE CAREFUL TO DO EVERYTHING WRITTEN IN IT. THEN YOU WILL BE PROSPEROUS AND SUCCESSFUL".
JOSHUA 1:8 NIV

"However difficult life may seem, there is always something you can do and succeed at"
Stephen Hawking

Weekly Thought/Action

HOW CAN YOU CULTIVATE MORE SUCCESS HABITS?
WHAT CAN YOU DO NOW?

DATE _____

_____
_____
_____
_____

DATE _____

_____
_____
_____
_____

DATE _____

_____
_____
_____
_____

DATE _____

_____
_____
_____
_____

DATE _____

_____
_____
_____
_____

DATE _____

_____
_____
_____
_____

DATE _____

_____
_____
_____
_____

WEEKLY GRATITUDE

DATE _____

I'M GRATEFUL FOR....

1. _____
2. _____
3. _____

DATE _____

I'M GRATEFUL FOR....

1. _____
2. _____
3. _____

DATE _____

I'M GRATEFUL FOR....

1. _____
2. _____
3. _____

DATE _____

I'M GRATEFUL FOR....

1. _____
2. _____
3. _____

DATE _____

I'M GRATEFUL FOR....

1. _____
2. _____
3. _____

DATE _____

I'M GRATEFUL FOR....

1. _____
2. _____
3. _____

DATE _____

I'M GRATEFUL FOR....

1. _____
2. _____
3. _____

• WEEK 16 • PEACE •

AFFIRMATIONS

I EMBRACE PEACE

I HAVE THE PEACE OF GOD WHICH SURPASSES
ALL UNDERSTANDING

I WELCOME PEACE INTO MY LIFE AND FEEL
CALM AND COMFORTABLE

I PUT ON THE PEACE THAT COMES FROM GOD
LIKE A GARMENT

MEDITATION

GOD SAYS …"PEACE I LEAVE WITH YOU; MY
PEACE I GIVE YOU. I DO NOT GIVE TO YOU AS
THE WORLD GIVES. DO NOT LET YOUR HEARTS
BE TROUBLED AND DO NOT BE AFRAID".
JOHN 14: 27 NIV

"Sky above, Land below, Peace within"
Unknown

Weekly Thought/Action

WHAT CAN YOU DO TO BRING MORE PEACEFUL MOMENTS INTO YOUR LIFE?

DATE _____

_____

_____

_____

_____

DATE _____

_____

_____

_____

_____

DATE _____

_____

_____

_____

_____

DATE _____

_____

_____

_____

_____

DATE _____

_____

_____

_____

_____

DATE _____

_____

_____

_____

_____

DATE _____

_____

_____

_____

_____

WEEKLY GRATITUDE

DATE _____

I'M GRATEFUL FOR....

1. _____
2. _____
3. _____

DATE _____

I'M GRATEFUL FOR....

1. _____
2. _____
3. _____

DATE _____

I'M GRATEFUL FOR....

1. _____
2. _____
3. _____

DATE _____

I'M GRATEFUL FOR....

1. _____
2. _____
3. _____

DATE _____

I'M GRATEFUL FOR....

1. _____
2. _____
3. _____

DATE _____

I'M GRATEFUL FOR....

1. _____
2. _____
3. _____

DATE _____

I'M GRATEFUL FOR....

1. _____
2. _____
3. _____

• WEEK 17 • HEALTH & HEALING •

AFFIRMATIONS

I GIVE NO PLACE TO SICKNESS AND PAIN IN MY BODY AS GOD HAS SENT HIS WORD AND HEALED ME

I EMBRACE EVERY OPPORTUNITY TO DO WHAT I NEED TO MAINTAIN 100% HEALTH

I AM HEALED BY THE STRIPES OF JESUS CHRIST

I LIVE IN ABUNDANT HEALTH AND WELLBEING

MEDITATION

GOD SAYS "I PRAY THAT YOU PROSPER IN ALL THINGS AND BE IN GOOD HEALTH EVEN AS YOUR SOUL PROSPERS"
3 JOHN 1:2 NKJV

"The question isn't how to get cured; but how to live"
Joseph Conrad

Weekly Thought/Action

WHAT NEW PRACTICE/HABITS CAN YOU EMBRACE THIS WEEK TO BOOST YOUR HEALTH AND WELLBEING?

DATE _____

_____
_____
_____
_____

DATE _____

_____
_____
_____
_____

DATE _____

_____
_____
_____
_____

DATE _____

_____
_____
_____
_____

DATE _____

_____
_____
_____
_____

DATE _____

_____
_____
_____
_____

DATE _____

_____
_____
_____
_____

WEEKLY GRATITUDE

DATE _____

I'M GRATEFUL FOR....

1. _____
2. _____
3. _____

DATE _____

I'M GRATEFUL FOR....

1. _____
2. _____
3. _____

DATE _____

I'M GRATEFUL FOR....

1. _____
2. _____
3. _____

DATE _____

I'M GRATEFUL FOR....

1. _____
2. _____
3. _____

DATE _____

I'M GRATEFUL FOR....

1. _____
2. _____
3. _____

DATE _____

I'M GRATEFUL FOR....

1. _____
2. _____
3. _____

DATE _____

I'M GRATEFUL FOR....

1. _____
2. _____
3. _____

AFFIRMATIONS

I EXPECT GREAT THINGS TO HAPPEN

I AM HOPEFUL OF A BRIGHT FUTURE

I AM ENTHUSIASTIC ABOUT THE DIRECTION OF MY LIFE

I EXPERIENCE LIMITLESS HOPE

MEDITATION

GOD SAYS "MAY THE GOD OF HOPE FILL YOU WITH ALL JOY AND PEACE AS YOU TRUST IN HIM, SO THAT YOU MAY OVERFLOW WITH HOPE BY THE POWER OF THE HOLY SPIRIT"
ROM 15:13 NIV

"Let your hopes, not your hurts shape your future"
Robert H Schuller

Weekly Thought/Action

WHAT ARE YOU HOPEFUL FOR RIGHT NOW?

DATE _____

_____
_____
_____
_____

DATE _____

_____
_____
_____
_____

DATE _____

_____
_____
_____
_____

DATE _____

_____
_____
_____
_____

DATE _____

_____
_____
_____
_____

DATE _____

_____
_____
_____
_____

DATE _____

_____
_____
_____
_____

WEEKLY GRATITUDE

DATE _____

I'M GRATEFUL FOR....

1. _____
2. _____
3. _____

DATE _____

I'M GRATEFUL FOR....

1. _____
2. _____
3. _____

DATE _____

I'M GRATEFUL FOR....

1. _____
2. _____
3. _____

DATE _____

I'M GRATEFUL FOR....

1. _____
2. _____
3. _____

DATE _____

I'M GRATEFUL FOR....

1. _____
2. _____
3. _____

DATE _____

I'M GRATEFUL FOR....

1. _____
2. _____
3. _____

DATE _____

I'M GRATEFUL FOR....

1. _____
2. _____
3. _____

• WEEK 19 • JOY •

AFFIRMATIONS

I EMBRACE JOY IN MY LIFE AND ALL I DO

I HAVE STRENGTH BECAUSE I HAVE THE JOY OF THE LORD

I LIVE A LIFE FULL OF JOY

MY HEART IS FILLED WITH JOY

MEDITATION

GOD SAYS: "THE YOUNG WOMEN WILL SHOUT FOR JOY AND THE MEN OLD AND YOUNG WILL JOIN IN THE CELEBRATION. I WILL TURN MOURNING INTO JOY. I WILL COMFORT THEM AND EXCHANGE THEIR SORROW FOR REJOICING."
JER 31:13 NLT

"Find out where joy resides and give it a voice beyond singing, for to miss the joy is to miss all"
Robert Louis Stevenson

Weekly Thought/Action

WRITE DOWN ALL THE THINGS, EVENTS, SITUATIONS
OR PEOPLE THAT BRING YOU JOY

DATE _____

_____
_____
_____
_____

DATE _____

_____
_____
_____
_____

DATE _____

_____
_____
_____
_____

DATE _____

_____
_____
_____
_____

DATE _____

_____
_____
_____
_____

DATE _____

_____
_____
_____
_____

DATE _____

_____
_____
_____
_____

WEEKLY GRATITUDE

DATE _____

I'M GRATEFUL FOR....

1. _____
2. _____
3. _____

DATE _____

I'M GRATEFUL FOR....

1. _____
2. _____
3. _____

DATE _____

I'M GRATEFUL FOR....

1. _____
2. _____
3. _____

DATE _____

I'M GRATEFUL FOR....

1. _____
2. _____
3. _____

DATE _____

I'M GRATEFUL FOR....

1. _____
2. _____
3. _____

DATE _____

I'M GRATEFUL FOR....

1. _____
2. _____
3. _____

DATE _____

I'M GRATEFUL FOR....

1. _____
2. _____
3. _____

• WEEK 20 • CONFIDENCE •

AFFIRMATIONS

I HAVE THE CONFIDENCE I NEED TO FEARLESSLY
BE MYSELF

I RADIATE CONFIDENCE

LOVING MYSELF GIVES ME CONFIDENCE

MY CONFIDENCE GROWS EACH DAY

MEDITATION

GOD SAYS "FOR THE LORD WILL BE YOUR
CONFIDENCE, AND WILL KEEP YOUR FOOT
FROM BEING CAUGHT"
PROV 3:26 NKJV

"Self-confidence is a superpower, once you start to
believe in yourself. Magic starts to happen"
Unknown

WEEKLY THOUGHT/ACTION

WHAT COULD YOU DO TO IMPROVE YOUR SELF-CONFIDENCE OR TO HELP OTHERS WITH THEIRS?

DATE _____

_____

_____

_____

_____

DATE _____

_____

_____

_____

_____

DATE _____

_____

_____

_____

_____

DATE _____

_____

_____

_____

_____

DATE _____

_____

_____

_____

_____

DATE _____

_____

_____

_____

_____

DATE _____

_____

_____

_____

_____

WEEKLY GRATITUDE

DATE _____

I'M GRATEFUL FOR....

1. _____
2. _____
3. _____

DATE _____

I'M GRATEFUL FOR....

1. _____
2. _____
3. _____

DATE _____

I'M GRATEFUL FOR....

1. _____
2. _____
3. _____

DATE _____

I'M GRATEFUL FOR....

1. _____
2. _____
3. _____

DATE _____

I'M GRATEFUL FOR....

1. _____
2. _____
3. _____

DATE _____

I'M GRATEFUL FOR....

1. _____
2. _____
3. _____

DATE _____

I'M GRATEFUL FOR....

1. _____
2. _____
3. _____

• WEEK 21 • VISION •

AFFIRMATIONS

I HAVE A CLEAR VISION FOR THE FUTURE

MY VISION FOR MY FUTURE IS WITHIN ME AND IT IS REAL

I HAVE WHAT IT TAKES TO TURN VISION INTO REALITY

ENVISIONING MY SUCCESS KEEPS ME ON THE RIGHT PATH

MEDITATION

GOD SAYS " WRITE THE VISION AND MAKE IT PLAIN ON TABLETS; THAT HE MAY RUN WHO READS IT"
HAB 2:2 NKJV

"Vision is the art of seeing
what is invisible to others"
Jonathan Swift

Weekly Thought/Action

CAPTURE YOUR DREAMS AGAIN. DREAM BIG!
TAKE A MINI-BREAK THIS WEEK IF YOU CAN

DATE _____

_____
_____
_____
_____

DATE _____

_____
_____
_____
_____

DATE _____

_____
_____
_____
_____

DATE _____

_____
_____
_____
_____

DATE _____

_____
_____
_____
_____

DATE _____

_____
_____
_____
_____

DATE _____

_____
_____
_____
_____

WEEKLY GRATITUDE

DATE _____

I'M GRATEFUL FOR....

1. _____
2. _____
3. _____

DATE _____

I'M GRATEFUL FOR....

1. _____
2. _____
3. _____

DATE _____

I'M GRATEFUL FOR....

1. _____
2. _____
3. _____

DATE _____

I'M GRATEFUL FOR....

1. _____
2. _____
3. _____

DATE _____

I'M GRATEFUL FOR....

1. _____
2. _____
3. _____

DATE _____

I'M GRATEFUL FOR....

1. _____
2. _____
3. _____

DATE _____

I'M GRATEFUL FOR....

1. _____
2. _____
3. _____

• WEEK 22 • EMOTIONS •

AFFIRMATIONS

I AM IN CHARGE OF HOW I FEEL

I ACCEPT MY EMOTIONS AND ALLOW THEM TO SERVE THEIR PURPOSE

I REMAIN CALM AND CENTERED IN ALL SITUATIONS

I PRIORITIZE MY EMOTIONAL WELLBEING

MEDITATION

GOD SAYS " HE WHO IS SLOW TO ANGER IS BETTER THAN THE MIGHTY; AND HE WHO RULES HIS SPIRIT; THAN HE WHO TAKES A CITY"
PROV 16:32 NKJV

"Take control of your emotions,
before your emotions take control of you".
Scott Dye

Weekly Thought/Action

WRITE DOWN HOW YOU FEEL EACH DAY THIS WEEK.
HOW COULD YOU MAKE THIS BETTER?

DATE _____

_____

_____

_____

_____

DATE _____

_____

_____

_____

_____

DATE _____

_____

_____

_____

_____

DATE _____

_____

_____

_____

_____

DATE _____

_____

_____

_____

_____

DATE _____

_____

_____

_____

_____

DATE _____

_____

_____

_____

_____

WEEKLY GRATITUDE

⊲◈⊳

DATE _____

I'M GRATEFUL FOR....

1. _____
2. _____
3. _____

DATE _____

I'M GRATEFUL FOR....

1. _____
2. _____
3. _____

DATE _____

I'M GRATEFUL FOR....

1. _____
2. _____
3. _____

DATE _____

I'M GRATEFUL FOR....

1. _____
2. _____
3. _____

DATE _____

I'M GRATEFUL FOR....

1. _____
2. _____
3. _____

DATE _____

I'M GRATEFUL FOR....

1. _____
2. _____
3. _____

DATE _____

I'M GRATEFUL FOR....

1. _____
2. _____
3. _____

• WEEK 23 • ENERGY •

AFFIRMATIONS

I AM FULL OF ENERGY AND ENTHUSIASM FOR LIFE

I DEVOTE MY TIME AND ENERGY INTO THINGS THAT MATTER

I PAUSE, RENEW AND RECHARGE MY ENERGY LEVELS WHEN I NEED TO

I PRIORITIZE MY TIME, ENERGY AND FOCUS

MEDITATION

GOD SAYS "I WILL REFRESH THE WEARY AND SATISFY THE FAINT"
JER 31:25 NIV

"Your energy is currency, spend it well, invest it wisely"
Unknown

Weekly Thought/Action

WRITE DOWN WHAT ENERGISES YOU.
WHAT ENERGISING ACTIVITIES CAN YOU TAKE ON THIS WEEK?

DATE _____

_____
_____
_____
_____

DATE _____

_____
_____
_____

DATE _____

_____
_____
_____

DATE _____

_____
_____
_____

DATE _____

_____
_____
_____

DATE _____

_____
_____
_____

DATE _____

_____
_____
_____

WEEKLY GRATITUDE

DATE _____

I'M GRATEFUL FOR....

1. _____
2. _____
3. _____

DATE _____

I'M GRATEFUL FOR....

1. _____
2. _____
3. _____

DATE _____

I'M GRATEFUL FOR....

1. _____
2. _____
3. _____

DATE _____

I'M GRATEFUL FOR....

1. _____
2. _____
3. _____

DATE _____

I'M GRATEFUL FOR....

1. _____
2. _____
3. _____

DATE _____

I'M GRATEFUL FOR....

1. _____
2. _____
3. _____

DATE _____

I'M GRATEFUL FOR....

1. _____
2. _____
3. _____

• WEEK 24 • CONTENTMENT •

AFFIRMATIONS

I CHOOSE TO BE CONTENT WITH MY LIFE

I FEEL JOY AND CONTENTMENT IN THE PRESENT MOMENT

I AM PEACEFUL, CALM AND CONTENTED

I CHOOSE TO KEEP MY NEEDS SIMPLE

MEDITATION

GOD SAYS "NOW GODLINESS WITH CONTENTMENT IS GREAT GAIN"
1 TIM 6:6 NKJV

" Happiness grows best
in the soil of contentment".
Tim Fargo

Weekly Thought/Action

EACH DAY, WRITE A LIST OF 3-5 THINGS
WHICH MAKE YOU HAPPY/ BRING YOU JOY

DATE _____

_____
_____
_____
_____

DATE _____

_____
_____
_____
_____

DATE _____

_____
_____
_____
_____

DATE _____

_____
_____
_____
_____

DATE _____

_____
_____
_____
_____

DATE _____

_____
_____
_____

DATE _____

_____
_____
_____

WEEKLY GRATITUDE

DATE _____

I'M GRATEFUL FOR....

1. _____
2. _____
3. _____

DATE _____

I'M GRATEFUL FOR....

1. _____
2. _____
3. _____

DATE _____

I'M GRATEFUL FOR....

1. _____
2. _____
3. _____

DATE _____

I'M GRATEFUL FOR....

1. _____
2. _____
3. _____

DATE _____

I'M GRATEFUL FOR....

1. _____
2. _____
3. _____

DATE _____

I'M GRATEFUL FOR....

1. _____
2. _____
3. _____

DATE _____

I'M GRATEFUL FOR....

1. _____
2. _____
3. _____

• WEEK 25 • TIME •

AFFIRMATIONS

MY TIME IS VALUABLE

TIME IS ON MY SIDE, SO I TAKE ADVANTAGE OF
EVERY SECOND

I MINIMISE TIME WASTING

I MANAGE MY TIME FOR SUCCESS

MEDITATION

GOD SAYS "SEE THEN THAT YOU WALK
CIRCUMSPECTLY, NOT AS FOOLS BUT AS WISE,
REDEEMING THE TIME, BECAUSE THE DAYS ARE
EVIL".
EPHESIANS 5:15-16 NKJV

"Time waits for no-one"
Folklore

Weekly Thought/Action

EVALUATE - HOW WELL DO YOU USE YOUR TIME? DO YOU NEED TO FIND MORE TIME IN YOUR SCHEDULE? HOW COULD YOU SAVE TIME? HOW COULD YOU FIND/CREATE MORE TIME?

DATE _____

_____
_____
_____
_____

DATE _____

_____
_____
_____
_____

DATE _____

_____
_____
_____
_____

DATE _____

_____
_____
_____
_____

DATE _____

_____
_____
_____
_____

DATE _____

_____
_____
_____
_____

DATE _____

_____
_____
_____
_____

WEEKLY GRATITUDE

DATE _____

I'M GRATEFUL FOR....

1. _____
2. _____
3. _____

DATE _____

I'M GRATEFUL FOR....

1. _____
2. _____
3. _____

DATE _____

I'M GRATEFUL FOR....

1. _____
2. _____
3. _____

DATE _____

I'M GRATEFUL FOR....

1. _____
2. _____
3. _____

DATE _____

I'M GRATEFUL FOR....

1. _____
2. _____
3. _____

DATE _____

I'M GRATEFUL FOR....

1. _____
2. _____
3. _____

DATE _____

I'M GRATEFUL FOR....

1. _____
2. _____
3. _____

• WEEK 26 • FAITH •

AFFIRMATIONS

I BELIEVE GOD DESIRES THAT I LIVE IN HEALTH
AND WELLBEING; AND I CHOOSE TO DO SO BY
HIS GRACE

IN MY MIDLIFE SEASON I AM HEALTHY IN BODY,
MIND, SOUL AND SPIRIT

I TRUST GOD TO HELP ME MAKE THE CHANGES
IN LIFESTYLE SO I CAN LIVE A VIBRANT MIDLIFE

I WILL NOT RELY ON MY WILLPOWER BUT CHOOSE
TO HAVE FAITH IN GOD TO HELP ME LIVE A LIFE OF
HEALTH, BALANCE AND WELLBEING

MEDITATION

GOD SAYS "....WITH GOD ALL THINGS ARE
POSSIBLE"
MATT 19.16 NIV

"Faith is like Wifi, it is invisible but has the power
to connect you to what you need"
Unknown

Weekly Thought/Action

REVISIT THE HEALTH AND WELLBEING GOALS YOU WROTE
EARLIER; EVALUATE AND WRITE DOWN WHERE YOU ARE WITH
THESE NOW.

DATE _____

_____
_____
_____
_____

DATE _____

_____
_____
_____
_____

DATE _____

_____
_____
_____
_____

DATE _____

_____
_____
_____
_____

DATE _____

_____
_____
_____
_____

DATE _____

_____
_____
_____
_____

DATE _____

_____
_____
_____
_____

WEEKLY GRATITUDE

DATE _____

I'M GRATEFUL FOR....

1. _____
2. _____
3. _____

DATE _____

I'M GRATEFUL FOR....

1. _____
2. _____
3. _____

DATE _____

I'M GRATEFUL FOR....

1. _____
2. _____
3. _____

DATE _____

I'M GRATEFUL FOR....

1. _____
2. _____
3. _____

DATE _____

I'M GRATEFUL FOR....

1. _____
2. _____
3. _____

DATE _____

I'M GRATEFUL FOR....

1. _____
2. _____
3. _____

DATE _____

I'M GRATEFUL FOR....

1. _____
2. _____
3. _____

• WEEK 27 • GRATITUDE •

AFFIRMATIONS

I AM THANKFUL FOR THIS DAY

I AM THANKFUL I AM ALIVE, HEALTHY AND WELL

I AM THANKFUL FOR AN ABUNDANT LIFE

I AM THANKFUL FOR MY FRIENDS AND FAMILY

MEDITATION

GOD SAYS "IN EVERYTHING GIVE THANKS
FOR THIS IS THE WILL OF GOD
IN CHRIST JESUS FOR YOU"
1 THESS 5:18 NKJV

"Gratitude turns what we have into enough"
Unknown

WEEKLY GRATITUDE

DATE _____

I'M GRATEFUL FOR....

1. _____
2. _____
3. _____

DATE _____

I'M GRATEFUL FOR....

1. _____
2. _____
3. _____

DATE _____

I'M GRATEFUL FOR....

1. _____
2. _____
3. _____

DATE _____

I'M GRATEFUL FOR....

1. _____
2. _____
3. _____

DATE _____

I'M GRATEFUL FOR....

1. _____
2. _____
3. _____

DATE _____

I'M GRATEFUL FOR....

1. _____
2. _____
3. _____

DATE _____

I'M GRATEFUL FOR....

1. _____
2. _____
3. _____

• WEEK 28 • LOVE •

AFFIRMATIONS

I LOVE MYSELF AND OTHERS WITH KINDNESS
AND PATIENCE

I AM COMPASSIONATE AND LOVE MYSELF

I BELIEVE I AM LOVED FOR WHO I AM

AS GOD LOVES ME, I AM ABLE TO LOVE OTHERS

MEDITATION

GOD SAYS: "ABOVE ALL, LOVE EACH OTHER
DEEPLY, BECAUSE LOVE COVERS OVER A
MULTITUDE OF SINS"
1ST PETER 4:8 NIV

"Love is not what you say, Love is what you do"
Unknown

WEEKLY THOUGHT/ACTION

EACH DAY WRITE DOWN 5 PEOPLE, THINGS OR PLACES YOU LOVE

DATE _____

_____
_____
_____
_____

DATE _____

_____
_____
_____
_____

DATE _____

_____
_____
_____
_____

DATE _____

_____
_____
_____
_____

DATE _____

_____
_____
_____
_____

DATE _____

_____
_____
_____
_____

DATE _____

_____
_____
_____
_____

WEEKLY GRATITUDE

DATE _____

I'M GRATEFUL FOR....

1. _____
2. _____
3. _____

DATE _____

I'M GRATEFUL FOR....

1. _____
2. _____
3. _____

DATE _____

I'M GRATEFUL FOR....

1. _____
2. _____
3. _____

DATE _____

I'M GRATEFUL FOR....

1. _____
2. _____
3. _____

DATE _____

I'M GRATEFUL FOR....

1. _____
2. _____
3. _____

DATE _____

I'M GRATEFUL FOR....

1. _____
2. _____
3. _____

DATE _____

I'M GRATEFUL FOR....

1. _____
2. _____
3. _____

• WEEK 29 • DIET •

AFFIRMATIONS

I WILL EAT HEALTHY PROTEIN AND HIGH FIBRE
FOODS THAT ADD TO MY FEELINGS OF
VIBRANCY

I EAT WELL TO SEND POSITIVE MESSAGES TO MY
BODY AND MIND AND KEEP THEM WELL

I CHOOSE TO FOCUS ON EATING MOSTLY PLANT-
BASED FOODS AND LEAN PROTEIN TO KEEP MY
ENERGY LEVELS HIGH

I MAKE POSITIVE CHANGES TO MY DIET WHICH
INVIGORATES AND MAKES ME VIBRANT

MEDITATION

GOD SAYS "SO WHETHER YOU EAT OR DRINK
OR WHATEVER YOU DO,
DO IT ALL FOR THE GLORY OF GOD"
1 COR 10:31 NIV

"The foods we choose, make a difference".
Michael Greger

Weekly Thought/Action

WHAT FOOD SWAPS HAVE YOU MADE/CAN YOU MAKE TO SUPPORT YOUR HEALTH? WHAT ARE YOUR FAVOURITE FOODS/RECIPES? ARE THESE HEALTHY? WHERE YOU CAN GET HELP WITH YOUR DIET?

DATE _____

_____
_____
_____
_____

DATE _____

_____
_____
_____
_____

DATE _____

_____
_____
_____
_____

DATE _____

_____
_____
_____
_____

DATE _____

_____
_____
_____
_____

DATE _____

_____
_____
_____
_____

DATE _____

_____
_____
_____
_____

WEEKLY GRATITUDE

❖

DATE _____

I'M GRATEFUL FOR....

1. _____
2. _____
3. _____

DATE _____

I'M GRATEFUL FOR....

1. _____
2. _____
3. _____

DATE _____

I'M GRATEFUL FOR....

1. _____
2. _____
3. _____

DATE _____

I'M GRATEFUL FOR....

1. _____
2. _____
3. _____

DATE _____

I'M GRATEFUL FOR....

1. _____
2. _____
3. _____

DATE _____

I'M GRATEFUL FOR....

1. _____
2. _____
3. _____

DATE _____

I'M GRATEFUL FOR....

1. _____
2. _____
3. _____

AFFIRMATIONS

I COMMIT TO REGULAR EXERCISE SO I AM
MENTALLY AND PHYSICALLY STRONG

AS I TAKE CARE OF MY BODY, I SEE A LOT OF
BENEFITS IN OTHER AREAS OF MY LIFE

I VARY MY EXERCISES, SO I GET ENJOYMENT
OUT OF MY WORKOUTS

I AM FIT IN BODY, MIND AND SPIRIT

MEDITATION

GOD SAYS "NO DISCIPLINE SEEMS PLEASANT AT THE
TIME, BUT PAINFUL. LATER ON, HOWEVER, IT PRODUCES
A HARVEST OF RIGHTEOUSNESS AND PEACE FOR THOSE
WHO HAVE BEEN TRAINED BY IT. THEREFORE,
STRENGTHEN YOUR FEEBLE ARMS AND WEAK KNEES"
HEB 12: 11-12 NIV

"Exercise in the morning, before your brain
figures out what you are doing".
Unknown

Weekly Thought/Action

IS YOUR EXERCISE ROUTINE CONSISTENT? IF NOT, HOW CAN YOU
MAKE IT CONSISTENT? WHAT HELP DO YOU NEED?

DATE _____

_____
_____
_____
_____

DATE _____

_____
_____
_____
_____

DATE _____

_____
_____
_____
_____

DATE _____

_____
_____
_____
_____

DATE _____

_____
_____
_____
_____

DATE _____

_____
_____
_____
_____

DATE _____

_____
_____
_____
_____

WEEKLY GRATITUDE

DATE _____

I'M GRATEFUL FOR....

1. _____
2. _____
3. _____

DATE _____

I'M GRATEFUL FOR....

1. _____
2. _____
3. _____

DATE _____

I'M GRATEFUL FOR....

1. _____
2. _____
3. _____

DATE _____

I'M GRATEFUL FOR....

1. _____
2. _____
3. _____

DATE _____

I'M GRATEFUL FOR....

1. _____
2. _____
3. _____

DATE _____

I'M GRATEFUL FOR....

1. _____
2. _____
3. _____

DATE _____

I'M GRATEFUL FOR....

1. _____
2. _____
3. _____

AFFIRMATIONS

I DEAL WITH STRESS CONSTRUCTIVELY

I REMAIN CALM TO PROTECT MY MENTAL AND PHYSICAL WELLBEING AT STRESSFUL TIMES

I MANAGE MY STRESS LEVELS, SO I THINK MORE CLEARLY AND PERFORM MORE EFFECTIVELY

I CALMLY RELEASE MY STRESS INTO THE WIND.

MEDITATION

GOD SAYS: "PEACE I LEAVE WITH YOU; MY PEACE I GIVE YOU. I DO NOT GIVE TO YOU AS THE WORLD GIVES. DO NOT LET YOUR HEARTS BE TROUBLED AND DO NOT BE AFRAID"
JOHN 14:27 NIV

"Give your stress wings; and let it fly away."

Terri Guillemets

Weekly Thought/Action

WHAT ARE THE WAYS YOU CAN RELEASE STRESS FROM YOUR LIFE? WRITE DOWN ONE OR MORE FOR EACH DAY THIS WEEK

DATE _____

_____

_____

_____

_____

DATE _____

_____

_____

_____

_____

DATE _____

_____

_____

_____

_____

DATE _____

_____

_____

_____

_____

DATE _____

_____

_____

_____

_____

DATE _____

_____

_____

_____

_____

DATE _____

_____

_____

_____

_____

WEEKLY GRATITUDE

DATE _____

I'M GRATEFUL FOR....

1. _____
2. _____
3. _____

DATE _____

I'M GRATEFUL FOR....

1. _____
2. _____
3. _____

DATE _____

I'M GRATEFUL FOR....

1. _____
2. _____
3. _____

DATE _____

I'M GRATEFUL FOR....

1. _____
2. _____
3. _____

DATE _____

I'M GRATEFUL FOR....

1. _____
2. _____
3. _____

DATE _____

I'M GRATEFUL FOR....

1. _____
2. _____
3. _____

DATE _____

I'M GRATEFUL FOR....

1. _____
2. _____
3. _____

• WEEK 32 • SLEEP •

AFFIRMATIONS

MY RESTFUL NIGHT'S SLEEP REPLENISHES ME.

THE REST AND RELAXATION FROM MY GOOD NIGHT'S SLEEP KEEPS ME FIT.

MY RESTFUL SLEEP GIVES MY BODY THE OPPORTUNITY TO HEAL

I SLEEP WELL TO BOOST MY IMMUNE SYSTEM.

MEDITATION

GOD SAYS "WHEN YOU LIE DOWN, YOU WILL NOT BE AFRAID; WHEN YOU LIE DOWN, YOUR SLEEP WILL BE SWEET"
PROV 3:24 NIV

"The shorter you sleep, the shorter your life"
Matthew Walker

Weekly Thought/Action

EACH NIGHT, WHICH ONE ACTIVITY THAT INTERFERES WITH YOUR
REGULAR BEDTIME CAN YOU AVOID?

DATE _____

_____
_____
_____
_____

DATE _____

_____
_____
_____
_____

DATE _____

_____
_____
_____
_____

DATE _____

_____
_____
_____
_____

DATE _____

_____
_____
_____
_____

DATE _____

_____
_____
_____
_____

DATE _____

_____
_____
_____
_____

WEEKLY GRATITUDE

DATE _____

I'M GRATEFUL FOR....

1. _____
2. _____
3. _____

DATE _____

I'M GRATEFUL FOR....

1. _____
2. _____
3. _____

DATE _____

I'M GRATEFUL FOR....

1. _____
2. _____
3. _____

DATE _____

I'M GRATEFUL FOR....

1. _____
2. _____
3. _____

DATE _____

I'M GRATEFUL FOR....

1. _____
2. _____
3. _____

DATE _____

I'M GRATEFUL FOR....

1. _____
2. _____
3. _____

DATE _____

I'M GRATEFUL FOR....

1. _____
2. _____
3. _____

• WEEK 33 • RELATIONSHIPS •

AFFIRMATIONS

I MAKE AND HAVE GOOD INTERPERSONAL
CONNECTIONS

I HAVE MANY VALUABLE RELATIONSHIPS WHICH
FILL ME WITH JOY

I LET GO OF ANY TOXIC, NEGATIVE OR
STRESSFUL RELATIONSHIPS

I APPRECIATE THOSE CLOSEST TO ME AND
VALUE THEIR LOVE AND AFFECTION

MEDITATION

GOD SAYS: "A NEW COMMAND I GIVE YOU: LOVE
ONE ANOTHER. AS I HAVE LOVED YOU, SO YOU
MUST LOVE ONE ANOTHER"
JOHN 13:34 NIV

"Friendship is the only cement that will
ever hold the world together".
Woodrow Wilson

WEEKLY THOUGHT/ACTION

EACH DAY, CONSIDER WHICH OF YOUR CONNECTIONS COULD USE
A LITTLE ATTENTION. GO AHEAD AND MAKE THOSE CONNECTIONS.

DATE _____

_____
_____
_____
_____

DATE _____

_____
_____
_____
_____

DATE _____

_____
_____
_____
_____

DATE _____

_____
_____
_____
_____

DATE _____

_____
_____
_____
_____

DATE _____

_____
_____
_____
_____

DATE _____

_____
_____
_____
_____

WEEKLY GRATITUDE

❖

DATE _____

I'M GRATEFUL FOR....

1. _____
2. _____
3. _____

DATE _____

I'M GRATEFUL FOR....

1. _____
2. _____
3. _____

DATE _____

I'M GRATEFUL FOR....

1. _____
2. _____
3. _____

DATE _____

I'M GRATEFUL FOR....

1. _____
2. _____
3. _____

DATE _____

I'M GRATEFUL FOR....

1. _____
2. _____
3. _____

DATE _____

I'M GRATEFUL FOR....

1. _____
2. _____
3. _____

DATE _____

I'M GRATEFUL FOR....

1. _____
2. _____
3. _____

• WEEK 34 • WEIGHT •

I MAKE MY HEALTH A PRIORITY AND MAINTAIN
A HEALTHY BODY WEIGHT

I LOSE WEIGHT AT A REASONABLE PACE

I COMMIT MYSELF TO HEALTHY WEIGHT-LOSS

I STAY AWAY FROM FAST, EASY FIXES AND FADS
TO SUSTAIN MY WEIGHT LOSS

MEDITATION

GOD SAYS: "......LET US LAY ASIDE EVERY WEIGHT,
AND THE SIN WHICH SO EASILY ENSNARES US,
AND LET US RUN WITH ENDURANCE THE RACE
THAT IS SET BEFORE US"
HEB 12:1 NKJV

"Beauty isn't measured in Lbs".
Unknown

Weekly Thought/Action

WHAT CHANGES HAVE YOU MADE OR CAN YOU MAKE TO HELP
WITH YOUR HEALTHY WEIGHT LOSS/GAIN?

DATE _____

_____
_____
_____
_____

DATE _____

_____
_____
_____
_____

DATE _____

_____
_____
_____
_____

DATE _____

_____
_____
_____
_____

DATE _____

_____
_____
_____
_____

DATE _____

_____
_____
_____
_____

DATE _____

_____
_____
_____
_____

WEEKLY GRATITUDE

DATE _____

I'M GRATEFUL FOR....

1. _____
2. _____
3. _____

DATE _____

I'M GRATEFUL FOR....

1. _____
2. _____
3. _____

DATE _____

I'M GRATEFUL FOR....

1. _____
2. _____
3. _____

DATE _____

I'M GRATEFUL FOR....

1. _____
2. _____
3. _____

DATE _____

I'M GRATEFUL FOR....

1. _____
2. _____
3. _____

DATE _____

I'M GRATEFUL FOR....

1. _____
2. _____
3. _____

DATE _____

I'M GRATEFUL FOR....

1. _____
2. _____
3. _____

• WEEK 35 • YOUR MIND •

AFFIRMATIONS

I FILL MY MIND WITH POSITIVITY, REJECT
NEGATIVITY AND SPREAD HOPE TO OTHERS

MY MIND AND THOUGHTS MAKE ME A SOLUTION-
FINDER, PEACEMAKER, DREAMER, AND GO GETTER

I GROW STRONGER IN MIND, BODY, AND SOUL
EACH DAY.

MY MIND IS A GREAT ASSET AND MAKES ME
CONCENTRATE AND FOCUS AT A HIGH LEVEL.

MEDITATION

GOD SAYS "...AND DO NOT BE CONFORMED TO THIS
WORLD, BUT BE TRANSFORMED BY THE RENEWING OF
YOUR MIND, THAT YOU MAY PROVE WHAT IS THAT
GOOD AND ACCEPTABLE AND PERFECT WILL OF GOD"
ROM 12:2 NKJV

"You have power over your mind, not outside
events; Realise this and you will find strength".
Marcus Aurelius

Weekly Thought/Action

HOW CAN YOU REFOCUS YOUR MIND ON THE POSITIVE, IF A
NEGATIVE THOUGHT TRIES TO SURGE? WHAT CAN/WILL YOU DO
TO STRENGTHEN YOUR MIND EACH DAY?

DATE _____

_____

_____

_____

_____

DATE _____

_____

_____

_____

_____

DATE _____

_____

_____

_____

_____

DATE _____

_____

_____

_____

_____

DATE _____

_____

_____

_____

_____

DATE _____

_____

_____

_____

_____

DATE _____

_____

_____

_____

_____

WEEKLY GRATITUDE

DATE _____

I'M GRATEFUL FOR....

1. _____
2. _____
3. _____

DATE _____

I'M GRATEFUL FOR....

1. _____
2. _____
3. _____

DATE _____

I'M GRATEFUL FOR....

1. _____
2. _____
3. _____

DATE _____

I'M GRATEFUL FOR....

1. _____
2. _____
3. _____

DATE _____

I'M GRATEFUL FOR....

1. _____
2. _____
3. _____

DATE _____

I'M GRATEFUL FOR....

1. _____
2. _____
3. _____

DATE _____

I'M GRATEFUL FOR....

1. _____
2. _____
3. _____

• WEEK 36 • ANXIETY •

AFFIRMATIONS

I BREATHE IN CALM AND I BREATHE OUT ANXIETY

EACH BREATH I TAKE CLEANSES MY MIND

STRESS AND ANXIETY LEAVE MY BODY AS I EXHALE

I RENEW MYSELF CONSTANTLY AS I BREATHE

MEDITATION

GOD SAYS "...BE ANXIOUS FOR NOTHING"
PHIL 4:6 NKJV

"Anxiety happens when you think you have to figure out everything all at once. Breathe. You're strong. You got this. take it day by day".
Karen Salmansohn

Weekly Thought/Action

HOW DO YOU MANAGE YOUR ANXIETY? WHAT NEW STRATEGIES
CAN YOU ADOPT TO HELP DEAL WITH ANXIETY?

DATE _____

_____
_____
_____
_____

DATE _____

_____
_____
_____
_____

DATE _____

_____
_____
_____
_____

DATE _____

_____
_____
_____
_____

DATE _____

_____
_____
_____
_____

DATE _____

_____
_____
_____
_____

DATE _____

_____
_____
_____
_____

WEEKLY GRATITUDE

DATE _____

I'M GRATEFUL FOR....

1. _____
2. _____
3. _____

DATE _____

I'M GRATEFUL FOR....

1. _____
2. _____
3. _____

DATE _____

I'M GRATEFUL FOR....

1. _____
2. _____
3. _____

DATE _____

I'M GRATEFUL FOR....

1. _____
2. _____
3. _____

DATE _____

I'M GRATEFUL FOR....

1. _____
2. _____
3. _____

DATE _____

I'M GRATEFUL FOR....

1. _____
2. _____
3. _____

DATE _____

I'M GRATEFUL FOR....

1. _____
2. _____
3. _____

AFFIRMATIONS

I TAKE CARE OF MYSELF SO I CAN BETTER TAKE CARE OF OTHERS IN MY LIFE

TREATING MYSELF WELL SENDS A POSITIVE IMPORTANT MESSAGE TO ME AND OTHERS

AS I TAKE GOOD CARE OF MYSELF MY SELF-ESTEEM INCREASES

I LOVE MYSELF AND RADIATE THIS LOVE TO OTHERS

MEDITATION

GOD SAYS "FOR NO ONE EVER HATED HIS OWN FLESH, BUT NOURISHES AND CHERISHES IT".
EPH 5:29 NIV

"You owe yourself the love that you so freely give others"
Unknown

Weekly Thought/Action

EACH DAY WRITE DOWN 5 PEOPLE, THINGS OR PLACES YOU LOVE

DATE _____

_____
_____
_____
_____

DATE _____

_____
_____
_____
_____

DATE _____

_____
_____
_____
_____

DATE _____

_____
_____
_____
_____

DATE _____

_____
_____
_____
_____

DATE _____

_____
_____
_____
_____

DATE _____

_____
_____
_____
_____

WEEKLY GRATITUDE

DATE _____

I'M GRATEFUL FOR....

1. _____
2. _____
3. _____

DATE _____

I'M GRATEFUL FOR....

1. _____
2. _____
3. _____

DATE _____

I'M GRATEFUL FOR....

1. _____
2. _____
3. _____

DATE _____

I'M GRATEFUL FOR....

1. _____
2. _____
3. _____

DATE _____

I'M GRATEFUL FOR....

1. _____
2. _____
3. _____

DATE _____

I'M GRATEFUL FOR....

1. _____
2. _____
3. _____

DATE _____

I'M GRATEFUL FOR....

1. _____
2. _____
3. _____

• WEEK 38 • SELF ESTEEM •

AFFIRMATIONS

I CHOOSE TO SEE AN ATTRACTIVE, THOUGHTFUL, INTELLIGENT, AND CARING PERSON.

EACH DAY I LEARN MORE ABOUT MYSELF AND I AM PLEASED WITH WHAT I DISCOVER

I VALUE MY SELF-WORTH

I AM MORE THAN ENOUGH

MEDITATION

GOD SAYS "YOU ARE ALTOGETHER BEAUTIFUL, MY LOVE; THERE IS NO FLAW IN YOU.
SONG OF SOLOMON 4:7 NIV

"Self-esteem is made up primarily of two things: feeling lovable and feeling capable"
Jack Canfield

Weekly Thought/Action

EACH DAY, LIST THINGS YOU CAN DO TO BOOST YOUR SELF ESTEEM

DATE _____

_____
_____
_____
_____

DATE _____

_____
_____
_____
_____

DATE _____

_____
_____
_____
_____

DATE _____

_____
_____
_____
_____

DATE _____

_____
_____
_____
_____

DATE _____

_____
_____
_____
_____

DATE _____

_____
_____
_____
_____

WEEKLY GRATITUDE

DATE _____

I'M GRATEFUL FOR....

1. _____
2. _____
3. _____

DATE _____

I'M GRATEFUL FOR....

1. _____
2. _____
3. _____

DATE _____

I'M GRATEFUL FOR....

1. _____
2. _____
3. _____

DATE _____

I'M GRATEFUL FOR....

1. _____
2. _____
3. _____

DATE _____

I'M GRATEFUL FOR....

1. _____
2. _____
3. _____

DATE _____

I'M GRATEFUL FOR....

1. _____
2. _____
3. _____

DATE _____

I'M GRATEFUL FOR....

1. _____
2. _____
3. _____

• WEEK 39 • WEALTH •

AFFIRMATIONS

I HAVE MULTIPLE STREAMS OF INCOME THAT ARE
BLESSED BY GOD

I AM FILLED WITH GOD'S WISDOM AND LED TO MAKE
WISE AND PROSPEROUS FINANCIAL DECISIONS

I AM BLESSED IN THE CITY, BLESSED IN THE FIELD,
BLESSED COMING IN & BLESSED GOING OUT. MY
BANK ACCOUNTS AND INVESTMENTS FLOURISH

AS I GIVE, IT IS GIVEN UNTO ME, GOOD MEASURE,
PRESSED DOWN, SHAKEN TOGETHER AND
RUNNING OVER

MEDITATION

GOD SAYS "THE BLESSING OF THE LORD BRINGS
WEALTH, WITHOUT PAINFUL TOIL FOR IT".
PROV 10:22 NIV

"Beware of small expenses, a small
leak will sink a great ship"
Benjamin Franklin

WEEKLY THOUGHT/ACTION

DO YOU HAVE DEBTS? WHAT IS YOUR DEBT REPAYMENT PLAN? ARE YOU
FINANCIALLY FREE? IF YES, HOW CAN YOU FURTHER INCREASE YOUR
INCOME? IF NO, WHAT IS YOUR 'FINANCIALLY FREE' FIGURE?

DATE _____

_____

_____

_____

_____

DATE _____

_____

_____

_____

_____

DATE _____

_____

_____

_____

_____

DATE _____

_____

_____

_____

_____

DATE _____

_____

_____

_____

_____

DATE _____

_____

_____

_____

_____

DATE _____

_____

_____

_____

_____

WEEKLY GRATITUDE

DATE _____

I'M GRATEFUL FOR....

1. _____
2. _____
3. _____

DATE _____

I'M GRATEFUL FOR....

1. _____
2. _____
3. _____

DATE _____

I'M GRATEFUL FOR....

1. _____
2. _____
3. _____

DATE _____

I'M GRATEFUL FOR....

1. _____
2. _____
3. _____

DATE _____

I'M GRATEFUL FOR....

1. _____
2. _____
3. _____

DATE _____

I'M GRATEFUL FOR....

1. _____
2. _____
3. _____

DATE _____

I'M GRATEFUL FOR....

1. _____
2. _____
3. _____

• WEEK 40 • SUCCESS •

AFFIRMATIONS

I LIVE A DISCIPLINED AND SUCCESSFUL LIFE

I FULLY ENJOY EACH SUCCESS THAT HAPPENS IN MY LIFE

I CELEBRATE MY SUCCESS, ENJOY EACH MOMENT AND SHARE IT WITH OTHERS.

I STAY CONSISTENT AS I WORK TOWARDS MY GOALS AND SUCCESS

MEDITATION

GOD SAYS " ….AND MAY THE LORD OUR GOD SHOW US HIS APPROVAL AND MAKE OUR EFFORTS SUCCESSFUL. YES, MAKE OUR EFFORTS SUCCESSFUL"
PS 90:17 NLT

"Some people dream of success, while others get up every morning and make it happen"
Wayne Huizenga

Weekly Thought/Action

WHAT SUCCESS HAVE YOU EXPERIENCED RECENTLY OR ARE YOU
LOOKING FORWARD TO? HOW HAVE OR DO YOU PLAN TO CELEBRATE OR
REWARD YOURSELF?

DATE _____

_____
_____
_____
_____

DATE _____

_____
_____
_____
_____

DATE _____

_____
_____
_____
_____

DATE _____

_____
_____
_____
_____

DATE _____

_____
_____
_____
_____

DATE _____

_____
_____
_____
_____

DATE _____

_____
_____
_____
_____

WEEKLY GRATITUDE

DATE _____

I'M GRATEFUL FOR....

1. _____
2. _____
3. _____

DATE _____

I'M GRATEFUL FOR....

1. _____
2. _____
3. _____

DATE _____

I'M GRATEFUL FOR....

1. _____
2. _____
3. _____

DATE _____

I'M GRATEFUL FOR....

1. _____
2. _____
3. _____

DATE _____

I'M GRATEFUL FOR....

1. _____
2. _____
3. _____

DATE _____

I'M GRATEFUL FOR....

1. _____
2. _____
3. _____

DATE _____

I'M GRATEFUL FOR....

1. _____
2. _____
3. _____

• WEEK 41 • ENERGY •

AFFIRMATIONS

I EXERCISE AND EAT WELL TO HELP BOOST MY ENERGY LEVELS

I STAY AWAY FROM NEGATIVITY TO PROTECT MY ENERGY

I RECOGNIZE ACTIVITIES AND PEOPLE THAT SAP MY ENERGY AND STAY AWAY FROM THEM

I AM FULL OF GOOD ENERGY AND ENTHUSIASM

MEDITATION

GOD SAYS " BUT THOSE WHO HOPE IN THE LORD WILL RENEW THEIR STRENGTH. THEY WILL SOAR ON WINGS LIKE EAGLES; THEY WILL RUN AND NOT GROW WEARY, THEY WILL WALK AND NOT BE FAINT".
IS 40:31 NIV

"Energy is contagious, either you affect people, or you infect people"
T Harv Eker

Weekly Thought/Action

WHAT ACTIVITIES/PEOPLE ARE ENERGY SAPS FOR YOU ?
WHAT STRATEGIES CAN YOU PUT IN PLACE TO REDUCE OR GET RID
OF THESE COMPLETELY?

DATE _____

_____
_____
_____
_____

DATE _____

_____
_____
_____
_____

DATE _____

_____
_____
_____
_____

DATE _____

_____
_____
_____
_____

DATE _____

_____
_____
_____
_____

DATE _____

_____
_____
_____
_____

DATE _____

_____
_____
_____
_____

WEEKLY GRATITUDE

DATE _____

I'M GRATEFUL FOR....

1. _____
2. _____
3. _____

DATE _____

I'M GRATEFUL FOR....

1. _____
2. _____
3. _____

DATE _____

I'M GRATEFUL FOR....

1. _____
2. _____
3. _____

DATE _____

I'M GRATEFUL FOR....

1. _____
2. _____
3. _____

DATE _____

I'M GRATEFUL FOR....

1. _____
2. _____
3. _____

DATE _____

I'M GRATEFUL FOR....

1. _____
2. _____
3. _____

DATE _____

I'M GRATEFUL FOR....

1. _____
2. _____
3. _____

• WEEK 42 • EXERCISE •

AFFIRMATIONS

MY EXERCISE GIVES ME CLARITY OF MIND

AS I VARY MY EXERCISE IT HELPS ME MAINTAIN A CONTINUOUS INTEREST IN FITNESS

MY SPIRITS SOAR AS EXERCISE BOOSTS MY MOOD.

AS I EXERCISE, I CONDITION MY HEART, INCREASE MY FLEXIBILITY AND TONE MY MUSCLES

MEDITATION

GOD SAYS "BODILY EXERCISE PROFITS".
1 TIM 4:8 NKJV

"The only bad workout is the one that didn't happen"
Unknown

Weekly Thought/Action

IS YOUR EXERCISE REGIME ON TRACK & CONSISTENT?
HOW CAN YOU IMPROVE ON WHAT YOU DO NOW?
WHAT ACTIONS WILL YOU TAKE?

DATE _____

_____
_____
_____
_____

DATE _____

_____
_____
_____
_____

DATE _____

_____
_____
_____
_____

DATE _____

_____
_____
_____
_____

DATE _____

_____
_____
_____
_____

DATE _____

_____
_____
_____
_____

DATE _____

_____
_____
_____
_____

WEEKLY GRATITUDE

DATE _____

I'M GRATEFUL FOR....

1. _____
2. _____
3. _____

DATE _____

I'M GRATEFUL FOR....

1. _____
2. _____
3. _____

DATE _____

I'M GRATEFUL FOR....

1. _____
2. _____
3. _____

DATE _____

I'M GRATEFUL FOR....

1. _____
2. _____
3. _____

DATE _____

I'M GRATEFUL FOR....

1. _____
2. _____
3. _____

DATE _____

I'M GRATEFUL FOR....

1. _____
2. _____
3. _____

DATE _____

I'M GRATEFUL FOR....

1. _____
2. _____
3. _____

• WEEK 43 • HOPE •

HOPE GUIDES MY CHOICES

MY HOPE IS RENEWED WITH EVERY SMALL BLESSING

I ALWAYS ALLOW HOPE TO SHINE IN MY LIFE

EACH DAY I CHOOSE HOPE OVER FEAR

MEDITATION

GOD SAYS "FOR I KNOW THE PLANS I HAVE FOR YOU," DECLARES THE LORD, "PLANS TO PROSPER YOU AND NOT TO HARM YOU, PLANS TO GIVE YOU HOPE AND A FUTURE."
JER 29:11 NIV

"Hope is being able to see that there is light despite all of the darkness".
Desmond Tutu

WEEKLY THOUGHT/ACTION

ARE THERE ANY SITUATIONS GOING ON NOW WHERE YOU NEED
TO REPLACE FEAR WITH HOPE? HOW CAN/WILL YOU DO THIS?

DATE _____

_____

_____

_____

_____

DATE _____

_____

_____

_____

_____

DATE _____

_____

_____

_____

_____

DATE _____

_____

_____

_____

_____

DATE _____

_____

_____

_____

_____

DATE _____

_____

_____

_____

_____

DATE _____

_____

_____

_____

_____

WEEKLY GRATITUDE

DATE _____

I'M GRATEFUL FOR....

1. _____
2. _____
3. _____

DATE _____

I'M GRATEFUL FOR....

1. _____
2. _____
3. _____

DATE _____

I'M GRATEFUL FOR....

1. _____
2. _____
3. _____

DATE _____

I'M GRATEFUL FOR....

1. _____
2. _____
3. _____

DATE _____

I'M GRATEFUL FOR....

1. _____
2. _____
3. _____

DATE _____

I'M GRATEFUL FOR....

1. _____
2. _____
3. _____

DATE _____

I'M GRATEFUL FOR....

1. _____
2. _____
3. _____

• WEEK 44 • JOY •

AFFIRMATIONS

MY MIND IS FOCUSSED ON THINGS OF JOY

I SEEK OUT OPPORTUNITIES AND ACTIONS THAT BRING ME JOY

TODAY, I SHOUT FOR JOY AND SING GOD'S PRAISES FOR HE HAS RANSOMED ME

JOY IS A CHOICE AND I CHOOSE JOY

MEDITATION

GOD SAYS "A CHEERFUL HEART IS GOOD MEDICINE".
PROV 17:22 NLT

"If you walk in joy; happiness is close behind".
Todd Stocker

Weekly Thought/Action

COMMIT TO DO AT LEAST ONE JOYFUL THING EACH DAY THIS
WEEK; CAPTURE THESE IN YOUR NOTES

DATE _____

_____
_____
_____
_____

DATE _____

_____
_____
_____
_____

DATE _____

_____
_____
_____
_____

DATE _____

_____
_____
_____
_____

DATE _____

_____
_____
_____
_____

DATE _____

_____
_____
_____
_____

DATE _____

_____
_____
_____
_____

WEEKLY GRATITUDE

DATE _____

I'M GRATEFUL FOR....

1. _____
2. _____
3. _____

DATE _____

I'M GRATEFUL FOR....

1. _____
2. _____
3. _____

DATE _____

I'M GRATEFUL FOR....

1. _____
2. _____
3. _____

DATE _____

I'M GRATEFUL FOR....

1. _____
2. _____
3. _____

DATE _____

I'M GRATEFUL FOR....

1. _____
2. _____
3. _____

DATE _____

I'M GRATEFUL FOR....

1. _____
2. _____
3. _____

DATE _____

I'M GRATEFUL FOR....

1. _____
2. _____
3. _____

AFFIRMATIONS

I AM VIBRANT, WELL, HEALTHY AND WHOLE

I AM THANKFUL FOR A HEALTHY BODY, MIND, SOUL AND SPIRIT

I AM HEALED BY THE STRIPES OF JESUS CHRIST

I LIVE IN ABUNDANT HEALTH AND WELLBEING

——— MEDITATION ———

GOD SAYS" 'NEVERTHELESS, I WILL BRING HEALTH AND HEALING TO IT; I WILL HEAL MY PEOPLE AND WILL LET THEM ENJOY ABUNDANT PEACE AND SECURITY."
JER 33:6 NIV

"It is health that is real wealth and not pieces of gold and silver."
Gandhi

WEEKLY THOUGHT/ACTION
CAPTURE WHAT OPTIMUM HEALTH AND WELLBEING MEANS FOR
YOU? WHAT ACTIONS CAN YOU TAKE TO MOVE TOWARDS THIS?

DATE _____

_____
_____
_____
_____

DATE _____

_____
_____
_____
_____

DATE _____

_____
_____
_____
_____

DATE _____

_____
_____
_____
_____

DATE _____

_____
_____
_____
_____

DATE _____

_____
_____
_____
_____

DATE _____

_____
_____
_____
_____

WEEKLY GRATITUDE

DATE _____

I'M GRATEFUL FOR....

1. _____
2. _____
3. _____

DATE _____

I'M GRATEFUL FOR....

1. _____
2. _____
3. _____

DATE _____

I'M GRATEFUL FOR....

1. _____
2. _____
3. _____

DATE _____

I'M GRATEFUL FOR....

1. _____
2. _____
3. _____

DATE _____

I'M GRATEFUL FOR....

1. _____
2. _____
3. _____

DATE _____

I'M GRATEFUL FOR....

1. _____
2. _____
3. _____

DATE _____

I'M GRATEFUL FOR....

1. _____
2. _____
3. _____

• WEEK 46 • PEACE •

AFFIRMATIONS

I HAVE PEACE WITHIN ME TO HELP QUIET ANY ANXIOUS THOUGHTS

I SEEK TO MAKE PEACE WITH ALL MY FAMILY, FRIENDS AND ASSOCIATES

I CREATE MORE MOMENTS OF PEACE FOR MYSELF AND OTHERS

GOD'S PEACE GUARDS MY HEART AND MIND

MEDITATION

GOD SAYS "......AND THE PEACE OF GOD, WHICH TRANSCENDS ALL UNDERSTANDING, WILL GUARD YOUR HEARTS AND YOUR MINDS IN CHRIST JESUS.
PHIL 4:7 NIV

"Go in the direction of where your peace is coming from"
C Joybell C

Weekly Thought/Action

COMMIT TO TAKE AT LEAST ONE MOMENT OF PEACE FOR
YOURSELF DURING EACH DAY, THIS WEEK, SCHEDULE THE TIME
AND WRITE IT DOWN SO IT ACTUALLY HAPPENS.

DATE _____

_____
_____
_____
_____

DATE _____

_____
_____
_____
_____

DATE _____

_____
_____
_____
_____

DATE _____

_____
_____
_____
_____

DATE _____

_____
_____
_____
_____

DATE _____

_____
_____
_____
_____

DATE _____

_____
_____
_____
_____

WEEKLY GRATITUDE

DATE _____

I'M GRATEFUL FOR....

1. _____
2. _____
3. _____

DATE _____

I'M GRATEFUL FOR....

1. _____
2. _____
3. _____

DATE _____

I'M GRATEFUL FOR....

1. _____
2. _____
3. _____

DATE _____

I'M GRATEFUL FOR....

1. _____
2. _____
3. _____

DATE _____

I'M GRATEFUL FOR....

1. _____
2. _____
3. _____

DATE _____

I'M GRATEFUL FOR....

1. _____
2. _____
3. _____

DATE _____

I'M GRATEFUL FOR....

1. _____
2. _____
3. _____

• WEEK 47 • PURPOSE •

AFFIRMATIONS

I BUILD MY LIFE AROUND MY PURPOSE

I RUN WITH PURPOSE IN EVERY STEP

I FEEL A DEEP SENSE OF PURPOSE FROM WHAT
I DO

I AM FILLED WITH PURPOSE

MEDITATION

GOD SAYS " FOR IT IS GOD WHO WORKS IN YOU
TO WILL AND TO ACT IN ORDER
TO FULFILL HIS GOOD PURPOSE".
PHIL 2:13 NIV

"The greatest tragedy is not death
but life without purpose"
Rick Warren

WEEKLY THOUGHT/ACTION

ARE YOU LIVING A LIFE OF PURPOSE? DO YOU KNOW WHAT YOU
WOULD LOVE TO DO FOR THE REST OF YOUR LIFE? TAKE TIME THIS
WEEK TO CAPTURE YOUR THOUGHTS ABOUT THIS

DATE _____

_____

_____

_____

_____

DATE _____

_____

_____

_____

_____

DATE _____

_____

_____

_____

_____

DATE _____

_____

_____

_____

_____

DATE _____

_____

_____

_____

_____

DATE _____

_____

_____

_____

_____

DATE _____

_____

_____

_____

_____

WEEKLY GRATITUDE

DATE _____

I'M GRATEFUL FOR....

1. _____
2. _____
3. _____

DATE _____

I'M GRATEFUL FOR....

1. _____
2. _____
3. _____

DATE _____

I'M GRATEFUL FOR....

1. _____
2. _____
3. _____

DATE _____

I'M GRATEFUL FOR....

1. _____
2. _____
3. _____

DATE _____

I'M GRATEFUL FOR....

1. _____
2. _____
3. _____

DATE _____

I'M GRATEFUL FOR....

1. _____
2. _____
3. _____

DATE _____

I'M GRATEFUL FOR....

1. _____
2. _____
3. _____

• WEEK 48 • CONFIDENCE •

AFFIRMATIONS

I HAVE CONFIDENCE IN MY SKILLS

I MAINTAIN MY APPEARANCE AND IT GIVES ME CONFIDENCE

I APPROACH THE DAY WITH ENTHUSIASM AND CONFIDENCE

I STAND IN MY AUTHENTIC POWER

MEDITATION

GOD SAYS "SUCH CONFIDENCE WE HAVE THROUGH CHRIST BEFORE GOD".
2 COR 3:4 NIV

"If you have no confidence in self; you are twice defeated in the race of life"
Marcus Garvey

Weekly Thought/Action

WHAT ONGOING SITUATION/S REQUIRE YOU TO BE MORE
CONFIDENT? HOW WILL YOU APPROACH THIS/THESE?

DATE _____

_____
_____
_____
_____

DATE _____

_____
_____
_____
_____

DATE _____

_____
_____
_____
_____

DATE _____

_____
_____
_____
_____

DATE _____

_____
_____
_____
_____

DATE _____

_____
_____
_____
_____

DATE _____

_____
_____
_____
_____

WEEKLY GRATITUDE

DATE _____

I'M GRATEFUL FOR....

1. _____
2. _____
3. _____

DATE _____

I'M GRATEFUL FOR....

1. _____
2. _____
3. _____

DATE _____

I'M GRATEFUL FOR....

1. _____
2. _____
3. _____

DATE _____

I'M GRATEFUL FOR....

1. _____
2. _____
3. _____

DATE _____

I'M GRATEFUL FOR....

1. _____
2. _____
3. _____

DATE _____

I'M GRATEFUL FOR....

1. _____
2. _____
3. _____

DATE _____

I'M GRATEFUL FOR....

1. _____
2. _____
3. _____

• WEEK 49 • VISION •

AFFIRMATIONS

I SUPPORT MY VISION WITH MY HABITS

I MEDITATE TO CLARIFY MY VISION

I HAVE A CLEAR VISION OF MY DREAMS AND GOALS

I HAVE A CLEAR PLAN TO ACHIEVE MY DREAMS

MEDITATION

GOD SAYS " WHERE THERE IS NO VISION, THE PEOPLE PERISH"
PROV 29:18 KJV

"Vision with action, makes a powerful reality".
Ron Kaufman

Weekly Thought/Action

TAKE TIME THIS WEEK TO REVISIT YOUR "LIFE'S VISION" AND CAPTURE YOUR
THOUGHT FOR EACH OF THESE AREAS OF YOUR LIFE: WORK/CAREER/BUSINESS,
MONEY, FRIENDS&FAMILY, PERSONAL DEVELOPMENT, PHYSICAL ENVIRONMENT,
HEALTH, LEISURE & PASTIMES, OTHER RELATIONSHIPS

DATE _____

DATE _____

DATE _____

DATE _____

DATE _____

DATE _____

DATE _____

WEEKLY GRATITUDE

DATE _____

I'M GRATEFUL FOR....

1. _____
2. _____
3. _____

DATE _____

I'M GRATEFUL FOR....

1. _____
2. _____
3. _____

DATE _____

I'M GRATEFUL FOR....

1. _____
2. _____
3. _____

DATE _____

I'M GRATEFUL FOR....

1. _____
2. _____
3. _____

DATE _____

I'M GRATEFUL FOR....

1. _____
2. _____
3. _____

DATE _____

I'M GRATEFUL FOR....

1. _____
2. _____
3. _____

DATE _____

I'M GRATEFUL FOR....

1. _____
2. _____
3. _____

• WEEK 50 • EMOTIONS •

AFFIRMATIONS

I AM IN CONTROL OF MY REACTIONS TO SITUATIONS

I RESIST NEGATIVE EMOTIONS TO RESIDE IN MY SOUL

I AM PATIENT, CALM, CONTENT AND ALLOW MY LIFE TO UNFOLD PEACEFULLY

I AM IN CHARGE OF HOW I FEEL

MEDITATION

GOD SAYS "DO NOT BE QUICKLY PROVOKED IN YOUR SPIRIT, FOR ANGER RESIDES IN THE LAP OF FOOLS".
ECCLES 7:9 NIV

"No matter the situation; never let your emotions overpower your intelligence"
Unknown

WEEKLY THOUGHT/ACTION

WHAT ACTIVITIES BOOST YOUR EMOTIONAL WELLBEING? AIM TO
DO AT LEAST ONE OF THESE EACH DAY THIS WEEK; SCHEDULE IN
THE TIME SO IT ACTUALLY HAPPENS

DATE _____

_____
_____
_____
_____

DATE _____

_____
_____
_____
_____

DATE _____

_____
_____
_____
_____

DATE _____

_____
_____
_____
_____

DATE _____

_____
_____
_____
_____

DATE _____

_____
_____
_____
_____

DATE _____

_____
_____
_____
_____

WEEKLY GRATITUDE

DATE _____

I'M GRATEFUL FOR....

1. _____
2. _____
3. _____

DATE _____

I'M GRATEFUL FOR....

1. _____
2. _____
3. _____

DATE _____

I'M GRATEFUL FOR....

1. _____
2. _____
3. _____

DATE _____

I'M GRATEFUL FOR....

1. _____
2. _____
3. _____

DATE _____

I'M GRATEFUL FOR....

1. _____
2. _____
3. _____

DATE _____

I'M GRATEFUL FOR....

1. _____
2. _____
3. _____

DATE _____

I'M GRATEFUL FOR....

1. _____
2. _____
3. _____

AFFIRMATIONS

I SEE SIMPLE THINGS AS BLESSINGS

I MAKE LIFE CHOICES THAT LEAD TO TRUE JOY AND HAPPINESS

I EXPERIENCE SATISFACTION IN ALL PARTS OF MY LIFE

I AM PEACEFUL, CALM AND CONTENTED

MEDITATION

GOD SAYS "I KNOW WHAT IT IS TO BE IN NEED, AND I KNOW WHAT IT IS TO HAVE PLENTY. I HAVE LEARNED THE SECRET OF BEING CONTENT IN ANY AND EVERY SITUATION, WHETHER WELL FED OR HUNGRY, WHETHER LIVING IN PLENTY OR IN WANT"
PHIL 4:12 NIV

"Simplicity is the first cousin of contentment"
John Stott

Weekly Thought/Action

THIS WEEK, TAKE SOME TIME TO "CLEAR OUT" THINGS YOU HAVEN'T USED IN THE LAST SIX MONTHS. HAVE A CLEAR OUT OF PAPER, CLOTHES AND ITEMS YOU COULD THROW AWAY OR DONATE. CLEAR OUT THE CLUTTER!

DATE _____

_____
_____
_____
_____

DATE _____

_____
_____
_____
_____

DATE _____

_____
_____
_____
_____

DATE _____

_____
_____
_____
_____

DATE _____

_____
_____
_____
_____

DATE _____

_____
_____
_____
_____

DATE _____

_____
_____
_____
_____

WEEKLY GRATITUDE

DATE _____

I'M GRATEFUL FOR....

1. _____
2. _____
3. _____

DATE _____

I'M GRATEFUL FOR....

1. _____
2. _____
3. _____

DATE _____

I'M GRATEFUL FOR....

1. _____
2. _____
3. _____

DATE _____

I'M GRATEFUL FOR....

1. _____
2. _____
3. _____

DATE _____

I'M GRATEFUL FOR....

1. _____
2. _____
3. _____

DATE _____

I'M GRATEFUL FOR....

1. _____
2. _____
3. _____

DATE _____

I'M GRATEFUL FOR....

1. _____
2. _____
3. _____

• WEEK 52 • THANKSGIVING •

AFFIRMATIONS

I CHOOSE TO MOVE THROUGH LIFE WITH A GRATEFUL HEART

MY DAILY ACTIONS ARE ROOTED IN THANKSGIVING

GIVING THANKS IS A NATURAL PART OF MY LIFE

AS I GIVE THANKS, I LIVE HAPPILY AND PEACEFULLY.

MEDITATION

GOD SAYS "OH, GIVE THANKS TO THE LORD,
FOR HE IS GOOD!
FOR HIS MERCY ENDURES FOREVER.
PS 107:1 NKJV

"Acknowledging the good you already have in your life is the foundation for all abundance"
Eckhart Tolle

Weekly Thought/Action

IN WHICH SITUATIONS IS IT DIFFICULT FOR YOU TO FOCUS ON BEING THANKFUL? WHAT ARE THE THINGS YOU ARE MOST THANKFUL FOR?

DATE _____

_____
_____
_____
_____

DATE _____

_____
_____
_____
_____

DATE _____

_____
_____
_____
_____

DATE _____

_____
_____
_____
_____

DATE _____

_____
_____
_____
_____

DATE _____

_____
_____
_____
_____

DATE _____

_____
_____
_____
_____

WEEKLY GRATITUDE

DATE _____

I'M GRATEFUL FOR....

1. _____
2. _____
3. _____

DATE _____

I'M GRATEFUL FOR....

1. _____
2. _____
3. _____

DATE _____

I'M GRATEFUL FOR....

1. _____
2. _____
3. _____

DATE _____

I'M GRATEFUL FOR....

1. _____
2. _____
3. _____

DATE _____

I'M GRATEFUL FOR....

1. _____
2. _____
3. _____

DATE _____

I'M GRATEFUL FOR....

1. _____
2. _____
3. _____

DATE _____

I'M GRATEFUL FOR....

1. _____
2. _____
3. _____

FINAL REFLECTIONS

WHAT HAVE YOU LEARNED? HOW HAVE YOU, OR YOUR LIFE
CHANGED? A SPACE TO REFLECT...

Statement of Faith

*We believe in God and His Son Jesus as our Lord and Personal Saviour

*We believe Gods intention is for all to live in Health and Wellbeing

*We believe God heals sickness and disease and makes us well and whole

If you would like to meet with the one who can make you happy, healthy, whole and commit your life to God and Jesus; all you have to do is believe in your heart and confess with your mouth and you will be saved.

If you want this for yourself please say the following prayer:

"Dear God, I know I have sinned against you and I ask forgiveness for all my sins. I believe that Jesus died for me on the cross and rose again. Lord Jesus, I commit my life to you, I invite you to come into my heart and I receive you as my Lord and Saviour. I am saved. Send your Holy Spirit to live in me and help me live my life for you forever. I ask this in Jesus Name Amen"

Congratulations! You are welcome into God's family. Please contact us so we can advise you on the next steps to take on your journey and walk with God.

About the Author

Bukky Ayoade

Menopause Specialist~Pharmacist~Certified Health Coach
Principal Consultant ~Vibrant Midlife Wellness Practice CIC

Bukky helps Women 40+ live a Vibrant Midlife ~ Healthy, Happy & Well

Aside from being a certified Health and Wellness Coach, her wellness coaching is underpinned by over 35 years of experience as a Pharmacist working in blue-chip pharmaceutical companies. She is Principal Consultant at Vibrant Midlife Wellness Practice CIC

Bukky has a special interest in lifestyle medicine and women's health - specifically the Menopause. With her unique, evidence and faith based expert system & coaching she has helped motivated women in midlife get fitter, healthier, slimmer, more confident, and fabulous by helping them create their personalised menopause care plan.   She is holistic in her approach and focuses on a client's body, mind and spirit.

She currently leads a workstream on the National Menopause programme at NHS England responsible for menopause support and interventions for the NHS workforce, with her team they have launched national menopause guidance and e-learning modules for staff & line managers

She also helps organisations support and retain highly skilled female talent through menopause awareness, workshops, coaching and consultancy. They are an asset!

Bukky is a dynamic and engaging speaker and has featured on various stages and platforms speaking on all things "Menopause, Women's Health & Wellbeing".

Contact Bukky via:
t: 0208 088 0895
w: vibrantmidlife.com/contact
IG: @vibrantmidlife
Facebook: https://www.facebook.com/groups/vibrantmidlife

Milton Keynes UK
Ingram Content Group UK Ltd.
UKHW020911211123
432927UK00006B/83